Transformations

A WOMAN'S JOURNEY OF SELF-DISCOVERY

Carol Juergensen Sheets ACSW, LCSW, CSAT, CCPS-C, PCC

Christine Tyro-Shields ACSW, LCSW, LCAC

SANO PRESS, LLC
LONG BEACH, CA

1st Edition

Cover image by Kittikorn PH, Adobestock.com, standard license. Cover image modified by Chris Bordey. Cover spread, book design, & layout by Chris Bordey.

All images and graphics from Flaticon.com, Pixabay.com, and Unsplash.com in accordance with Creative Commons CC0 except where noted. *Stomach Icon* by Nikita Golubev, Flaticon.com. *Heart Icon* by Freepik, Flaticon.com. Adobestock.com images in use with standard license. Graphics & Illustrations pp. 14-15, 45, 47, 49, 51, 56, 59, and 71 by Chris Bordey. *Ammanda* font commercial license obtained from Creativefabrica.com. *Lucy Rounded* font desktop license with commercial use obtained from Creativemarket.com. All other fonts in use with commercial license from Ultimatefontdownload.com, Fontesk.com, and system fonts. Sano Press feather trademark
Sano Press, LLC.

ISBN-13: 978-1-7339222-6-5

TABLE OF CONTENTS

1. Introduction

Why This Work Will Change Your Life

"THE SUCCESS OF EVERY WOMAN SHOULD BE THE INSPIRATION TO ANOTHER. WE SHOULD RAISE EACH OTHER UP. MAKE SURE YOU'RE VERY COURAGEOUS: BE STRONG, BE EXTREMELY KIND, AND ABOVE ALL BE HUMBLE." - SERENA WILLIAMS

Within yourself, you possess everything you need to change your life, but you may feel that something is keeping you from realizing your own true greatness. As therapists, we have found some predictable issues that tend to prevent women from recognizing their personal self-worth, strength, and power. women know all too well how to care for others, but often lack the ability to take care of themselves or to ask directly for what they need emotionally. In our work with over 2,000 groups of women and thousands of women individually, we have developed certain exercises that have been shown to allow women to unlock their personal power and make the necessary changes to create the life they deserve. We'll share these exercises in the pages that follow.

The exercises were specifically created to help women decrease reliance on individual therapy, while promoting healthy self-esteem in day-to-day life. This journey is therapeutically sound and promotes self-growth and change. You will be amazed at the breakthroughs that occur as you feel your feelings, identify what you want, and create a sense of self-awareness that naturally activates the skills to make your cherished dreams in life happen.

This workbook will teach you the skills to manage anger, promote self-esteem and assertiveness, and deal with pivotal family-of-origin issues that will move you into the progressive stages of change. we have found that quite often childhood trauma or neglect prevents women from knowing and embracing their greatness. This workbook will propel you forward in your journey.

In this workbook you will learn creative strategies and work through exercises that utilize anchoring, visualization, psychodrama, re-scripting, reframing, and meditation, as well as experiential techniques. Additional techniques are drawn from narrative therapy, metaphor therapy, hypnotherapy, and art therapy, all of which have been used as a catalyst for change. They work when you work them.

At the end of the workbook, we have listed some books that will assist you further in your journey for personal development. Both of us have personally read the books, done the work, and always looked for opportunities to take our lives to the next level. we want that for you and hope that you find this workbook to be a safe place for self-discovery!

Breaking the Chains of Codependency

PUTTING YOURSELF FIRST

women historically assume blame and responsibility for issues and emotions that are not their own. we believe that the self-awareness gained by working in this journal creates powerful insights that can propel you ahead in life.

Since women all too often put others' needs ahead of their own, they lose a sense of their own feelings, power, and identity. This journal will teach you how to detach from intense emotion, which serves to break the chains of codependency.

"WHERE THERE IS NO STRUGGLE, THERE IS NO STRENGTH" – OPRAH

You may find that there are predictable themes in your life, including:

- fear of conflict

- low self-esteem and/or poor self-identity

- lack of support

- inability to express feelings

- control issues

- childhood core issues

    - parental alcoholism/drug addiction

    - cycle of abuse (physical, sexual, and/or emotional)

    - parenting your parent

    - parental neglect/abandonment

    - overly critical parent

    - trauma

Clearly, this is not an exhaustive or all-inclusive list, yet these themes may present themselves repeatedly in your life. We have found that no matter where you are in your own personal journey, the exercises in this journal will no doubt help you grow and develop into a stronger, more empowered woman!

PERSONAL LIFE SKILL EXERCISES

These exercises teach you valuable skills that include learning how to:

- experience someone's anger without taking it personally

- build conflict regulation and resolution skills

- identify the five primary emotions (anger, sadness, happiness, fear and loneliness) to reduce feeling overwhelmed by a myriad of feelings

- process feelings in a healthy way and mobilize the needed strength and energy to direct your life

- assert and communicate your feelings and needs

- utilize re-parenting skills to maximize potential

- develop and embrace your own self-identity and uniqueness as a woman

- enhance character strengths that empower you to create the life you envision

- lessen the impact and control that depression and anxiety have in your life

- decrease codependency while increasing self-care

- increase the ability to meet personal needs

2. Identify Your Strengths

"THINK LIKE A QUEEN. A QUEEN IS NOT AFRAID TO FAIL." — OPRAH

Developing Personal Identity and Self-Esteem

As you do your work, it will be helpful to create a vision statement to shape a realistic, genuine, and healthy view of yourself. We recognize that as a woman, you may find it difficult to identify positive attributes about yourself. Often women exist with an extremely distorted view of themselves, which alters their self image and dominates their interactions with others. Historically, women have not been encouraged to verbalize and acknowledge their own strengths. Know that while you are completing these exercises, you are not only changing your own personal concept, you are beginning to change the attitudes and perceptions of the women who follow in your footsteps and the legacy of future generations of women.

WHAT IS A WOMAN?

The "What Is a Woman?" exercise allows you to clarify how you see yourself. It is a non-threatening way of self-discovery. In this activity, we have generated many adjectives (not nouns or roles) that describe a woman. These adjectives describe the many qualities that you possess, and you will also find that these attributes describe your mother, your sister, your best friend, and other women who have influenced you throughout your life.

Think about the positive and negative personality strengths that describe women. Personalize the exercise by asking yourself what words you would use to describe yourself. Then add to the list any adjectives that would describe your mother, sister, best friend, mentor, teacher, etc.

Add as many words as you can think of, have fun with it, and don't second-guess yourself! If your list is primarily negative, we would ask you to think about a woman that you admire and add positive words that describe her. As you read through the following list, circle those words that apply to your personality and character traits. We also ask that you add at least ten other adjectives to your list. Get creative! Begin this activity on the next page.

As you read through the list, circle the words that describe you.

giving foolish

PRACTICAL

AWESOME

ARROGANT wise narcissistic Purposeful

SUPPORTIVE fussy Spiritual

ENGAGING independent

ANGRY OPEN HARSH STRONG

PLAYFUL

Whiny Inspiring

RUDE

devoted AUTHENTIC

CARING RESILIENT PERSISTENT CLINGY

CONSISTENT needy ANXIOUS

JEALOUS

STUBBORN dependable lonely

GRUMPY Generous

empathetic ineffective cruel

Brilliant MEAN

Encouraging Faithful

Passionate bitter OVER-WHELMED sexual

LOVING

hopeful pathetic boring miserable

CRITICAL unhappy

HYPERSENSITIVE moody Trust-worthy

weak

Joyful
DILIGENT
HOSTILE
ISOLATED
friendly CHAOTIC CREATIVE
depressed *impatient* passive
Accepting ENTHUSIASTIC
Compassionate insecure
EMPOWERED polite Intelligent
NURTURING GUARDED
IMPULSIVE DUTIFUL
Judgmental e n v i o u s
CONNECTED
narrow-minded
dependent
humorous CONTROLLING
asexual *greedy* COWARDLY
COMPETITIVE depleted
intuitive Bitchy suspicious
SELFISH EMOTIONAL
POWERFUL TIRED
UNDER-
STANDING thankful

ADD AT LEAST 10 MORE ADJECTIVES:

If you find that you have primarily circled negative words, we ask that you review the list and pick out at least three to five additional words that describe your strengths. It is common for women to second-guess or doubt the positive words and not want to include them in their list. Circle the positive words, even if your critical voice tells you that you do not deserve to "claim" them.

After you have circled the adjectives that describe yourself and have added at least ten additional adjectives, complete the following statements by using those adjectives. Limit your choice of adjectives to no more than two words per statement. women are renowned for fragmenting or fracturing themselves. This exercise is meant to focus you on your identity at present.

As a woman,
I am

As a woman,
I am not

_____

_____

_____

As a woman,
I want to be

_____

_____

_____

CREATE A GOAL STATEMENT

Once you have completed the statements, read them out loud to see how they resonate with you. The final statement, "As a woman, I want to be..." now becomes your vision of yourself as you continue on your path of personal transformation.

To further anchor this new sense of identity, post this statement in highly visible places, like your refrigerator and your mirror. You may also find that creating a collage or vision board will reinforce this self-discovery. Visual images have a powerful influence on our conscious and subconscious minds and can help us change our lives!

Don't underestimate the power of your third statement, which is really an affirmation of who you want to be. Retraining the brain to recognize your strengths is a powerful tool to evoking change and personal transformation. If you find yourself really having difficulty, you might add the words "in the process of," which infers that you are a work in progress!

- "As a woman, I want to be strong," becomes...

  o   As a woman, I am in the process of gaining strength.

  or

- "As a woman, I want to be assertive," becomes...

  o   As a woman, I am in the process of being assertive.

Women are often unclear about what they want in their lives. Additionally, you may be unsure as to what goals to work on. The final statement in the "What Is a Woman?" activity allows you to own what you want to work toward on your own personal journey! The following examples illustrate this point:

- As a woman, I am weak and dependent.

- As a woman, I am not powerful.

- As a woman, I want to be strong.

Acknowledging the negative beliefs first helps clear the path so we can get to the positive ones.

This becomes not only your anchor—your vision—but a goal statement that you will explore throughout this workbook. By raising this to your conscious awareness, you can actively pursue creating the life you desire and deserve.

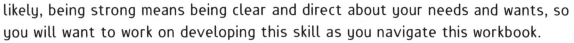

You may not be consciously aware of this, but you are articulating a goal of assertiveness. Ask yourself, "what additional skills am I learning by being strong?" Most likely, being strong means being clear and direct about your needs and wants, so you will want to work on developing this skill as you navigate this workbook.

Your anchor will guide you throughout this workbook but, more importantly, throughout life. Your theme will be reiterated throughout your personal journey. Therapeutically, this workbook provides and creates many opportunities for you to push beyond what you believe are your limitations or weaknesses.

The next step is to visualize what you want to become and how you want to shift at this time in your life.

Retrain Your Brain

Retraining your brain to see your positive attributes takes practice and patience. It can be an exciting process to create your self-identity in order to be the woman you were meant to be. Imagine that you could paint a canvas of who you wanted to be. As a painter, you have the capability to enhance your strengths and portray yourself as a strong, powerful woman.

well, the truth of the matter is that you are already strong and creative; you are intelligent and strategic. Perhaps you are simply lacking the reminders that will retrain the brain to have belief in yourself.

USE YOUR UNCONSCIOUS

The unconscious is a very powerful tool and when it repeatedly experiences a visual image, it goes into overdrive to make that vision a reality. You truly are the creator of your life and you can create the life you deserve.

THE NAME GAME

Use the letters of your name to create a visual of your strengths on the computer. If you struggle with identifying positive words, choose some words listed in the "what is a woman?" exercise. we have provided two examples for you.

C – Compassionate

A – AWESOME

R – RESILIENT

O – OPEN

L – Loving

C – Connected

H – HOPEFUL

R – RESILIENT

I – Intelligent

S – Spiritual

T – Thankful

I – Interdependent

N – Nurturing

E – Encouraging

Add artwork to your name, enlarge the font, and make it an expression of your affirmation. Get creative and place it somewhere where you will see it often to remind you of your personal greatness.

3. Develop Your Vision

"IF YOU DON'T RISK ANYTHING, YOU RISK EVEN MORE." – ERICA JONG

What Do You Need to Self-Actualize?

Most women are scheduled so tightly, they have very little time to listen to their intuition, a practice which can guide them into deep transformation. To tap into your purpose—your vision—you must find time daily to contemplate, reflect, and breathe.

Perhaps you already have a clear idea of the transformations you would like to see in your life, or maybe you are not sure what direction you should move. Either way, spend a few moments each day in quiet reflection to allow your visions of yourself to surface. After centering yourself, spend some time writing about your thoughts. The act of writing it down is the first step in making your visions a reality.

Through completing this exercise, one woman became aware that her life was off balance as she juggled her hectic schedule and roles as a mother, business owner, and spouse. Prior to the exercise, she thought she needed to be more efficient in her life. what she learned from the exercise was that she needed more balance to better care for herself. She was amazed at what her intuition told her when she slowed down enough to listen to what was within.

what is your personal vision for yourself and your own life?

Carving some time out of your schedule daily for meditating, contemplating, and reflecting will help you be more successful with this exercise and with progressing toward your vision. To develop that habit, consider the following:

- what time of day or night would work best for you to sit quietly for five to ten minutes in deep thought? As you create this daily practice, you may find a desire for more time in contemplation. It will be vital for you to convey to your family that this needs to be uninterrupted time – just for yourself.

- what place can you designate as your sacred spot to meditate? Do you have a favorite room? The yard? The patio?

- what supports can you utilize to give yourself uninterrupted time? Arrange with your partner to watch the kids; commit a specific time to minimize distractions and interruptions; etc.

CREATE A VISION BOARD

Become the architect of your life! Beginning with the positive descriptive words you identified in the "Name Game" exercise, cut out pictures, symbols, and words that reflect and depict those adjectives. Imagine that you could design your life visually by creating a collage that embraces the woman you are and/or the woman you want to be in the future. Think about the many dreams and goals you have for your life and find pictures that reflect the life you are currently living or want to grow into. Playfully have fun with this project and imagine that what you create on the paper could become your reality. Examining your vision board for five minutes a day allows for a deeper imprint on your subconscious.

A vision board is a collection of pictures and symbols that represent what you want in your life. It is like a collage or map of how you envision your life in the future.

What would you put on your vision board? What goals, aspirations, and dreams do you have? Would you like to change jobs, have better relationships with your kids or your significant other, find a life partner? Would you like to improve your health, lose some weight, become clearer and more direct? Would you like to increase your confidence, let go of your anger, or forgive someone?

In a very visual sense, the vision board depicts what you want to attract in your life. Begin by finding pictures of healthy relationships; strong, confident women; activities that promote fitness; etc.

This exercise is fun because it shows you the possibilities for your life ahead—how it is going to be different with your new focus and new direction.

Now grab an assortment of magazines, get out your scissors and glue or tape, and create that vision board. When you're done, place it in a spot where you can regularly see it. Then step back and watch it work its magic. Be sure to take a picture of your vision board, print it and paste or tape to the following page.

You may ask how a piece of your artwork could make a real impact on your life. The vision board provides an opportunity for you to retrain the brain and envision a different path in your life. It reminds you of the possibilities.

Paste your vision board here!

4. Increase Your Resilience

*"WE MUST BELIEVE THAT WE ARE GIFTED FOR SOMETHING,
AND THAT THIS THING, AT WHATEVER COST,
MUST BE ATTAINED." – MARIE CURIE*

Strengthening Your Self-Esteem

As you continue your journey, consider whether you see yourself as someone who has high self-esteem or low self-esteem, or somewhere in-between. The exercises in your workbook can help increase self-esteem no matter where you see yourself right now. If you have low self-esteem, you may need to spend some extra time in this chapter.

Low self-esteem generally occurs for two reasons. It may be a result of how you were raised or invalidated as a child. The second greatest contributor to low self-esteem is the significant events that have occurred as you were growing up in childhood or young adulthood. You can't change your past ... but you can choose to build your strengths!

The good news is that if you suffer from low self-esteem, you as an adult, can heal from the wrongs that happened to you in your past. Although it does take work, discipline, and a positive belief that you are worth it to increase self-esteem, it is achievable.

BE GENTLE WITH YOURSELF

The number one statement women make when they have low self-esteem is, "I am not good enough." Did you receive or experience a lot of negative messages as a child? This may have left you feeling disempowered and "less than." Perhaps your parents were discouraging or told you that you could not accomplish things in your life. Just as insidious, they may not have been available to you. Perhaps your parents were not around to validate you or identify your strengths. This typically happens when a parent is an alcoholic, a workaholic, or narcissist. It can be difficult as a child to build positive self-esteem in the face of that reality.

As an adult, you need to identify your strengths and remind yourself of your own potential. This may look like the following:

1. Remind yourself daily of your own internal strengths. This means looking in the mirror and telling yourself that you are confident, capable, kind-hearted, smart, intuitive, and loving.

2.   Practice making statements to yourself that an ideal parent would have told you as you were growing up.

Here are some examples of what that may sound like:

- "I know you don't feel like you can ask for the promotion, but truly you are ready for this assignment and would do an excellent job performing your new work duties."

- "I know you're afraid to date since your nasty divorce, but you have so much to offer another person and need to practice having fun with the opposite sex."

Talking to yourself as an ideal parent or a dear friend reminds you to be kinder and gentler to yourself as well as have the courage to take the risks necessary to have the experiences you deserve. Additionally, many women experience losses that erode their self-esteem, losses such as their parents' divorce, the inability to go to college, their own divorce, fractured relationships, or the death of a child.

In these types of situations, it is important to be your own best cheerleader. This might look like the following:

- You are on your way home from work and you get a speeding ticket. Instead of telling yourself you're stupid, unobservant and a screw-up, you tell yourself that this was a good life lesson to remember to slow down and that perhaps this saved you from an accident if you had continued to speed.

- Your husband asks you for a divorce. You feel rejected, sad, and worthless as a wife. This circumstance would require that you look at how you can grow from the situation and how you might ultimately be better off single. You might tell yourself that this will give you a chance to learn more about yourself, spend more time with the kids, and explore what you really want in life.

It may sound unrealistic, but it works if you work it. The important thing is to practice these skills regularly so that they become a natural part of your coping and prompt you to feel good about yourself no matter the circumstance. Be your own cheerleader. Your self-esteem will thank you!

The following exercises will help you further enhance your self-identity, increase your self-esteem, allow you to process core issues, and improve your body image, etc.

INCREASE YOUR RESILIENCE

Many women tend to get stuck or mired in the past, continually replaying negative situations or feelings. When this occurs, the future seems less hopeful. It becomes more challenging to see that the struggles of the past truly allow for the gifts of today. Take Oprah for example. As she celebrated the opening of her leadership school for girls in South Africa, she was able to recognize that the vision for this school was a culmination of all her life experiences, including that of being sexually abused and living in poverty. Oprah was able to transform her pain of childhood into a passion for empowering females all over the world.

One of the most important skills a woman can master is resiliency. Resilience is the capacity to recover from difficulties or the ability to see the positive in any situation. We must be able to see that we are the sum of all our life experiences, good and bad, joyful and sorrowful—that we have attained a certain wisdom from all of our life circumstances. Resilience is what makes us not just survivors, but women who thrive despite past adversity.

Part of your self-exploration will be learning new skills that will teach you about your own inner strength that resulted from your past. Take some time to think about how your life circumstances have made you the woman you are today.

Looking back allows you to acknowledge and embrace your history, or as we prefer to call it, your "her-story." What difficulties have you had in your life? What obstacles have you faced? What demons have you encountered? In essence, what is your her-story?

For this next exercise, we have provided a series of questions to answer prior to writing your her-story. They are designed to help you identify your resiliency.

What are the defining moments in my life?

What did these life experiences teach me about who I am?

How have I grown stronger as a result of these significant life events?

What did I learn about myself through those experiences?

How have I been shaped or imprinted by my childhood?

What are the life lessons that have carried me into my adulthood?

Be sure to include the lessons that you have learned as well as the actual life events. After writing her-story, one woman realized that as a result of growing up with a rage-aholic mother, she had actually gained a Teflon coating that allowed her to reject the hostility and projections of others. From this exercise, she was able to embrace the gift received rather than focus on the pain inflicted by her mother's rage.

WRITE YOUR HER-STORY

Take as much time as you need to write your life her-story. You may find that the words flow easily on paper, or you may need to go slowly bit by bit, writing about segments of your life (such as childhood, adolescence, young adulthood, and middle age).

write your personal her-story:

"YOUR STORY IS WHAT YOU HAVE. IT IS SOMETHING TO OWN."
— MICHELLE OBAMA

MY PERSONAL HER-STORY

MY PERSONAL HER-STORY (cont.)

MY PERSONAL HER-STORY (cont.)

5. Feeling Identification

"FEELINGS ARE LIKE WAVES, WE CAN'T STOP THEM FROM COMING BUT WE CAN CHOOSE WHICH ONES TO SURF." — UNKNOWN

Your Primary Feeling Can Motivate You

Do you feel stuck? Are there areas of your life that stay the same despite your desire to change? Do you wonder why you just can't get over the hurdles and make your life different?

Your emotions may be what are holding you back from becoming the woman you really want to be. To identify your feelings, it is helpful to reduce the emotions to five basic feelings:

- anger

- sadness

- happiness

- loneliness

- fear

You may prefer to identify your feelings with the following kid-friendly words. Since the first three rhyme, it is easy to remember the "famous five feelings."

- mad

- sad

- glad

- lonely

- afraid

All emotions can be reduced to any of these "famous five feelings." The difficult task is to determine which feeling is predominant at the time. You may be aware that you feel several feelings at one time. Oftentimes, the feeling most uncomfortable for you is the one you avoid. Women typically feel and express sadness when their main feeling is really anger. Men typically report anger when the uncomfortable feeling is generally fear or sadness.

Where do you feel personally stuck? Take a few moments and think of a situation that is problematic. Which feeling comes through the strongest when you think of this situation?

_____

_____

_____

_____

_____

_____

_____

_____

_____

_____

Three feelings that typically stop women from moving through their issues are anger, fear, and sadness. It is imperative that you identify what feeling is really immobilizing you. Doing this will motivate you to take care of yourself differently.

Here are some examples:

- A woman feels betrayed when her husband has an affair. She feels sad and depressed. Yet when she sits with the feelings, she realizes she is angry that he cheated on her. She can no longer trust him. This woman needed to feel anger instead of sadness. It gives her adrenaline to start working on how she was going to recover from the betrayal. Staying stuck in the sadness leaves her feeling lethargic. It keeps her in the victim role.

when she gets in touch with her anger, she begins to focus on herself and she sets aside time specifically to look at what she needs if she is going to become a single mother. She uses the anger to energize her into taking better care of herself, which includes activities such as playing tennis and attending church more regularly.

- A woman has lost her job through the downsizing process at work. She is 54 years old, has worked for the company for eighteen years, and expresses genuine anger at being dispensable. As she sits with her feelings, she finds that fear is actually her primary feeling. She is worried that she will be unable to find another job. She fears that it will alter her family's lifestyle. She is afraid that her friends will look at her differently if she remains unemployed

  As she examines her fears, she finds that she will be able to use techniques to rebuild her confidence and look at her life differently. She decides she will pursue real estate and buy low-income properties. She worked on her budget and refinanced her assets, and two years later she is financially solvent, pursuing a dream that becomes a reality by default. Identifying her fear helped her to realize her potential.

Don't let your feelings confuse you. Identify them and then use them to propel you toward your desired transformation.

what situation have you encountered and felt personally overwhelmed by?

_____

_____

_____

_____

_____

TRANSFORMATIONS: A WOMAN'S JOURNEY TO SELF-DISCOVERY

what was the primary feeling and how did it affect your choices?

_____

_____

_____

_____

_____

_____

How could you use your feelings to motivate you to make some needed changes?

_____

_____

_____

_____

_____

_____

Feelings Check-In

We find that women are so busy and so used to multitasking most of their waking day that they are left fragmented and forget to check in with their own needs and wants. The following exercises allow you to assess how you feel and what you want, which helps you to direct your energies as to what is best for you in your daily living.

THE DAILY FEELINGS CHECK-IN FORMAT

The following format allows you to take some quiet time each day and assess what your intention is. This simple tool empowers you to put yourself on the front burner and decide how you want to live your day and what direction you want to take for the day. It is a simple exercise of self-empowerment. Our belief is that when you tune in to what you need, you will be more likely to have enough energy for both yourself and others.

The daily "Feelings Check-In" allows you to

1.   be in the moment

2.   pay attention to what is going on inside of you

3.   nurture yourself

4.   let go of all things of which you have no control

The "Feelings Check-in" is the vehicle that allows you an opportunity to reflect. It is important for you to check in with your feelings and expectations on a daily basis and to encourage yourself to be accountable for your life.

The format is quite simple and is as follows on page 52...

Feelings Check-In

RIGHT HERE & NOW, I FEEL (*CIRCLE ONE*):

MAD   SAD   GLAD   LONELY   AFRAID

WHAT I APPRECIATE IN MY LIFE RIGHT NOW IS:

HOW I CAN APPROACH THE DAY TO FEEL MORE EMPOWERED:

WHAT I MAY NEED TO LET GO OF TO BE MORE FULLY PRESENT:

The 24-Hour Reflection

Pick one primary feeling to list in your check-in, even if you're experiencing all five feelings. Women are already so fragmented, we take little time to focus our attention on one, and only one, issue or feeling. This exercise provides an opportunity to do so. If you are like most women, you are typically flooded by a host of feelings. It is important to remind yourself that emotions fall into one of the five feeling categories

ANGER		*MAD*
SADNESS		**SAD**
HAPPINESS	*or*	**GLAD**
LONELINESS		**LONELY**
FEAR		**AFRAID**

Identifying your primary feeling (whether you use the adult version on the left or the kid version on the right), allows you to focus on one single emotion. When you are flooded with emotions, it's easier to become immobilized or paralyzed by them. The details of your life paint the picture and set the stage, but they are not the essence of healing and transformation—your feelings are!

Writing out your feelings can help ground you in the "here and now," as well as gently remind you of your desire to transform into the woman you want to become. It is helpful to reflect on your past twenty-four hours in order to better focus on the changes you want to make in your next twenty-four hours.

The format is quite simple and is as follows on the next page...

24-Hour Reflection

RIGHT HERE & NOW, I FEEL (CIRCLE ONE):

MAD   SAD   GLAD   LONELY   AFRAID

IN THE PAST 24 HOURS, I HAVE FELT:

ONE THING THAT I WILL FOCUS ON TODAY TO IMPROVE MY SENSE OF SELF:

ONE THING THAT I AM WILLING TO LET GO OF TODAY THAT IS NOT WITHIN MY CONTROL:

24-Hour Reflection

RIGHT HERE & NOW, I FEEL *(CIRCLE ONE)*:

(MAD)   SAD   GLAD   LONELY   AFRAID

I feel angry because I am taking care of the kids while my husband is off playing cards with his buddies.

BRIEF DESCRIPTION OF THE PAST 24 HOURS:

I have been really tired, as I have stayed up late with the baby and have done nothing for myself.

ONE THING THAT I WILL FOCUS ON TODAY TO IMPROVE MY SENSE OF SELF:

I will call Jill and ask if she will come over so that I can run some errands and go to the gym for some exercise.

ONE THING THAT I AM WILLING TO LET GO OF TODAY THAT IS NOT WITHIN MY CONTROL:

I will let go of my resentment toward my husband for meeting his needs and refocus on taking better care of mine.

FEELINGS COLOR CALENDAR

We know that feelings are neither good nor bad, they just are. Colors also are neither good nor bad, they just are . . . so add a little color to your feelings.

Assign colors to your feelings. One woman chose:

- anger—red

- sad—blue

- happy—yellow

- lonely—purple

- afraid/anxious—green

Now it's your turn. You may easily have colors in mind that represent your feelings. If not, close your eyes and think of a situation that caused you to feel each of the feelings below. Allow a color to come to mind and write it down. Remember there is no right or wrong color assignment.

- anger _____

- sad _____

- happy _____

- lonely _____

- afraid/anxious _____

Once you have your feeling colors identified, then begin to log your feelings color calendar daily. You may choose to use a paper calendar or create one on your computer. Get some markers, colored pens or pencils to use actual colors. Each day, color the block on a calendar to represent your primary feeling for the day. You may find it is one solid color, or you may split the block to represent the shifts that occur. For instance, you may have felt happy (yellow) in the morning, but sad (blue) throughout the rest of the day. The color calendar provides a quick visual to examine how you are feeling, which allows you to honor how you are feeling. Additionally, it allows you to choose what you can do to meet your needs to work through the anger, sadness, loneliness or fear that you may be feeling.

6. Accountability & Integrity

"THE CHALLENGE IS NOT TO BE PERFECT...
IT'S TO BE WHOLE." – JANE FONDA

Your Accountability and Integrity Check-In

What we know about women is that if they attend to their feelings, take time to be in the present, and then hold themselves accountable to some very important values, they will feel more confident and self-assured and better able to meet their needs.

First it is vital to acknowledge and feel the feelings but know that you are not your feelings!

The following checklist will help you hold yourself accountable and carry yourself with integrity. When focusing on yourself, you will find that it is most important to be true to yourself. As simple as that sounds, it can be a challenge to commit to writing in your journal every day. Don't put too much pressure on yourself; write as little or as much as you like, and let go of any self-judgment.

This workbook is a place for you to practice being authentically honest without fear of conflict arising. It allows you to take a deeper look at who you are as a woman as well as who you want to be.

Take a look at the following guidelines for accountability and integrity as well as for communication. Circle the statements that you believe you do well. After you have circled those strength areas, go back and star (*) the areas that you want to improve. What we know to be true is that the more you practice these techniques in your journal, the more likely you will be able to communicate to those that you love.

GUIDELINES FOR ACCOUNTABILITY AND INTEGRITY

- Take responsibility for yourself.

- Tell the truth.

- Avoid gossip.

- Do your personal best.

- Give yourself permission to rest and relax.

- Forgive yourself when you aren't at your best every day. This takes time and practice!

GUIDELINES FOR COMMUNICATION

You will have a better sense of integrity if you communicate honestly and openly with others and use the following principles as a guideline for being true to yourself.

- **Practice Assertiveness, Use Your Voice**. It may be unnatural at first to be assertive, but the more you practice this skill, the easier it becomes.

- **Be Aware of Your Feelings**. Work toward expressing them. Because avoidance of feelings is so ingrained, give special attention to how you feel and express yourself with feeling statements such as "I feel happy" or "I feel afraid."

- **Be Here and Now**. Emphasize the present. As much as possible, focus on your experience of the here and now. There is much research that shows that the happiest, most content people are those who stay in the present.

- **Use "I" Statements**. Rather than using the editorial "we" or "you," speak for yourself: "I feel angry."

- **Self-Reflect and Avoid Asking Questions**. "Why?" leads to analyzing and often leads away from emotions. Before asking the question "Why?" consider the statement behind the question and then express the direct statement. For example, instead of asking "Why am I always wanting more?" acknowledge to yourself, "I realize there is more I need to do to get my needs met."

- **Avoid Judgments—Be Descriptive**. Describe what you notice about yourself and be aware of your self-critical statements. If you find you are judging yourself, stop and gently give yourself permission to restate your observation, allowing room for imperfections. In this way, you do not place blame on yourself, and you begin to view yourself differently so that you accept your humanness. For example, instead of saying or writing, "I am a failure," say "I feel overwhelmed when I can't get it all done."

As you are doing the work, remember to:

- **Guard Your Confidentiality**. Keep your journal in a safe place where you can be assured that no one else will read it without your permission. You might even want to get a diary with a key.

- **Be Prepared**. We often walk through life in a half-dazed state, unaware of true ourselves and others. Transforming your life requires you to be alive and attentive. Be prepared to work hard and be enthusiastic about the changes you will make.

- **Create Support**. We are social beings. We were not designed to be isolated in our lives. Plan to create a support network with people you trust or build on your existing network.

THIS IS YOUR LIFE!
Commit yourself to making changes as if your life depended on it! The best way to predict your future is to create it!

7. Connect with your Inner Self

"COURAGE STARTS WITH SHOWING UP AND LETTING OURSELVES BE SEEN." – BRENÉ BROWN

Guided Meditation

Guided meditation is a form of visualization that allows you to experience your own internal process. Women are infamous for attending to everyone else's needs at the expense of their own. The guided meditation experience allows you to quiet yourself and to reflect on your thoughts, feelings, and emotions. We happen to believe that meditation allows you to connect to your intuition and your relationship with your higher power, the universe, or God. When you have a stronger connection to yourself and spirit, you are more likely going to be "inspired-in spirit" to see the world differently and to behave differently...with more confidence and certainty!

> *"LIFE IS NOT EASY FOR ANY OF US. BUT WHAT OF THAT? WE MUST HAVE PERSEVERANCE AND ABOVE ALL CONFIDENCE IN OURSELVES. WE MUST BELIEVE THAT WE ARE GIFTED FOR SOMETHING AND THAT THIS THING MUST BE ATTAINED."*
> — MARIE CURIE

Many of the problems that plague women are rooted in childhood issues. This visualization intentionally takes you back to your childhood so you can connect with your emotions as well as begin to develop a sense of hope that you can provide healing and support on your ongoing journey.

We have created a meditation that will put you in touch with issues surrounding sexuality, womanhood, depression, and the need for support. The clear and embedded message is this:

> "Your life can be different, and you can create the support you need!"

You may understand this on a conscious level and act on it immediately or you may need to grieve the loss of what you never had as a child. Simply allow the unconscious to imagine how you can take care of yourself presently and learn from what you did not get as a child. This meditation reinforces the power within all women and the intuitive process you possess to make the needed changes in your life.

- Set the atmosphere as you prepare for this meditation.

- Find a time when there will be no interruptions and you can spend ten to fifteen minutes for more quieting your thoughts. (Some women set a timer so they don't have to keep track of the time.)

- Dim the lights, light a candle, set an intention and choose some soothing soft background music.

- Take at least three deep breaths to relax and center yourself.

- Read over the meditation included on the next page.

- Then, close your eyes and focus inwardly, quietly listening to what is within – see what images, words, feelings and thoughts surface as you reflect on the meditation.

- You may choose to record the meditation yourself, or ask a friend to record it for you, as it may be soothing to hear your friend's voice guide your inward journey.

THE MEDITATION

This is an opportunity for you to quiet your thoughts and find that place of centered stillness that allows you to get in touch with all of your wisdom and your knowledge, taking this opportunity to listen to what is deep inside.

Imagine a color that you can breathe in that represents strength, love, and a gentle knowingness that you have everything you need to manifest all that is deep inside. The feminine process is an amazing gift that you were given. To be a woman has afforded you the special gift of growth, intuition, and relationship building. You have the ability to be so attuned to the needs of others, and yet this is your time to listen to the needs that are within you to recharge and replenish. How would your life be different if you started to regularly attend to your own needs and wants, and if you put yourself first so that you regularly had more to give? Who might you become?

Think back to what it was like to be a young adult, an adolescent, a school-age girl, or perhaps a toddler learning to take her first step. Find a safe place to visit each one of those stages in your awesome development. Who was there for you? What was that person like, and what did they do to reassure you that you were perfect just the way you were? We all have someone who has been that special person...go back to that place now and experience that person and the support that was given to you. What would it have been like if you could have received a steady stream of encouragement? What might you have done?

Can you imagine how you might have viewed your life differently had the different stages of your life been celebrated for the life experience that you incurred?

Imagine what it would have been like to have your family celebrate the feminine process as your body began to change and develop. Imagine that the instrumental people in your life were there for you and took you out to celebrate the beginning of your menstrual cycle. How might that have affected your femininity, your sexuality and your view of your womanhood?

When you turned eighteen, what events took place to shape the woman that you had become? Although there was much to learn, how did it feel to come into your own and realize that you had decisions that were solely yours to make?

And now that you are a woman who has come into your own, how might you do things differently so that you can feel the well-deserved feelings of accomplishment, contentment, and self-love? So that as you move into that contemplative season of life, you can be the kind of woman who can support and validate others? Because the true essence of being a woman requires that you nurture yourself with the same attention that you use when you take care of others.

How might you right some of the pressures you may have put on yourself for not being attractive or smart or strong enough in the past? What if you were finally to know that you are absolutely perfect the way you are? All the things that you have viewed as imperfections are really what have helped you develop the character to be the woman you are today. If there are things in your past that have tormented you or made you sad, as an adult woman you have the capability to release them from your spirit and move on in your journey.

And there may even be wrongs that you feel that you have done, and you can release those as they no longer serve you. Allow yourself the opportunity to be imperfect and release all the pain, burden, and sorrow so that you can see yourself with more self-love and assuredness. You can accept yourself more unconditionally and smile with a gentle knowingness that you are all that you were meant to be, that your worth does not depend on your accomplishments, nor does it require that your legacy be known to all. Instead, your brilliance is because you have done the best you could and made a difference in the lives of others that you have loved.

Can you accept that you are perfect, no matter what has occurred in your life? You are the woman you have strived to become!

we recommend that you read your meditation out loud and record it on your phone so that you can listen to it daily to remind yourself that you are powerful beyond measure!

JOURNAL YOUR INSIGHTS FROM THE MEDITATION

As you begin to return to this room, this space, allow yourself to begin to hear the outside sounds around you, the noises of the room, the sound of your own breathing, and anything else that is occurring outside of your meditative space. Set the intention for the meditation. what do you intend to accomplish?

Journal your thoughts about the meditation. what are you being guided to feel, see or do? Perhaps you are being encouraged to employ something that promotes better intentional self-care. You may be nudged to change something about you or your environment. whatever it is, write it down.

_____

_____

_____

_____

_____

_____

_____

_____

_____

Use a Transitional Object to Anchor Yourself

Transitional objects ground a woman in the present. We have worked with women in groups and given them an opportunity to pick a stone that speaks of their strength. You may choose pictures of a special family member, friend or mentor to remind you of the connection of support. Other women have chosen a cross, or a plaque with a special saying to empower them. You might want to build a small shrine or altar as a sacred space. You may ask yourself, "How does one attain more confidence and self-assuredness to be the woman I want to be?" We have found that women do better when they have the proper structure and support in their lives.

This means you need to organize your life to allow for time to journal on a consistent basis, find quiet time to reflect and contemplate, and create an environment that encourages you to take care of yourself.

- Do you journal regularly? Journaling allows you to stay focused on you.

- Do you have a picture that captures your love of life or energy?

- How about some refrigerator material that reminds you of how strong you are?

Support includes having healthy people who love and care about you; having them affirm that your feelings, thoughts, and beliefs are important, as well as having them remind you of all that you need to acknowledge and validate them. When women feel vulnerable, they may tend to isolate. In those times, it becomes vital to reach out to friends when you need support.

That is why we encourage you to create ways to remind yourself of your uniqueness and worthiness. For example, we would ask you to find an object that represents the new woman that you are becoming. Find a special poem or writing that honors you, or put your vision board somewhere that you can see it frequently. Those visual reminders provide inspiration.

We all need things that inspire us. What inspires you?

_____

_____

_____

_____

_____

You especially need inspiration to work through the tough stuff and release yourself from your anger and the conflict that you may have felt in the past. The next chapter will inspire you to work through residual feelings from your past.

8. Power of Self

Channeling Anger & Conflict into Power

*"WE DO NOT NEED MAGIC TO CHANGE THE WORLD,
WE CARRY ALL THE POWER WE NEED INSIDE OURSELVES ALREADY:
WE HAVE THE POWER TO IMAGINE BETTER."
- J.K. ROWLING*

How to Identify, Work Through, and Grow from Conflict

There are many exercises that can help release you from your past and assist you in recognizing the wisdom and power you have gained from your core issues. This chapter includes exercises that will address overt and covert anger, past and current abuse, fear of conflict, poor self-esteem and trauma.

When you work on these exercises, you will break free of old behaviors and create new ones like the following:

- interrupting self-defeating patterns and focusing on your resiliency

- creating self-awareness so that you can interrupt unhealthy behaviors and intentionally create alternative healthy behaviors

- learning how to accept conflict versus personalizing it and feeling inadequate, inferior, and unworthy

- establishing accountability to yourself which promotes a commitment for change

The personal work is intense, and many psychological layers will be excavated through this journey of self-exploration. You have the opportunity to become extremely honest with yourself in order to create strategies to change your life in dramatic ways.

The exercises presented in this chapter are a compilation of processes we have experienced in our own personal development as strong women and in our professional work with women. As you are journaling, let your imagination, creativity, and strong intuition guide you!

Here are some of the themes you will be exploring:

- social isolation

- codependency

- boundary setting

- assertiveness

- self-mutilation and self-destructive behaviors

- body image issues

- abandonment

- conflict avoidance

- over-responsibility

"I AM WILLING TO PUT MYSELF THROUGH ANYTHING; TEMPORARY PAIN OR DISCOMFORT MEANS NOTHING TO ME AS LONG AS I CAN SEE THAT THE EXPERIENCE WILL TAKE ME TO A NEW LEVEL. I AM INTERESTED IN THE UNKNOWN, AND THE ONLY PATH TO THE UNKNOWN IS THROUGH BREAKING BARRIERS, AN OFTEN PAINFUL PROCESS."
— *DIANA NYAD*

THE CONTAINER

Trust is a basic, yet vital need of all individuals. If you have grown up in an environment that was unsafe physically, sexually, or emotionally, your trust in others has been breached. This can impact your ability to trust even yourself—to not trust that all the answers you need lie within you.

This journal becomes a safe "container" for you to do your work.

Journaling is a safe way to identify feelings that in the past have blocked you from empowerment. As you utilize these techniques and exercises, take time to journal your feelings to process them and grow stronger from them.

Anger Exercises

Many women struggle with depression or anxiety. This can actually be suppressed or internalized anger that was never allowed to be expressed or verbalized. Both nature and nurture play a part in these conditions. We know in many cases there is a genetic link to depression and anxiety, and we also know that these conditions may also be situationally or environmentally induced. The good news is that, regardless of their origin, there are many ways to treat these conditions. Exercise, healthy diet, and support are among your first lines of defense for overcoming these struggles. For those who suffer more chronically, counseling along with medication may be instrumental in treating your depression or anxiety.

Another important aspect to feeling sad or fearful in life is to acknowledge the emotion. Since we know that depression can also be "anger turned inward," it is no surprise that you may have trouble seeing that you even have any anger in your life. Or it may be that you were not encouraged or permitted to express your anger for traumatic events that occurred during your childhood, such as parental alcoholism, abuse, or neglect. This journal is a safe place to begin "connecting" with the missing emotional link in your life—YOUR ANGER!

Acknowledging and expressing anger allows you to emotionally vomit, which often provides much catharsis from the anger and resentment you may have carried around for years or even decades. If you are one who denies feeling any anger, we encourage you to consider what injustices there may be in your life. You may find that this brings up repressed and suppressed anger, often from childhood trauma or from being raised in a home where anger was not an acceptable or safe emotion to have or express.

Anger work is intense, powerful, and liberating! For some, just talking about the emotion and referencing anger work can create anxiety and will send you running. You must prepare for this work by realizing that anger is normal and necessary. When expressed directly and in a non-destructive way, anger will have a positive impact on your life.

Anger is simply a buildup of adrenaline and must be released. It is that energy that protects in a fight-or-flight situation. Anger is vital to our survival...as individuals, and as women.

YES-NO: THE POWER CONNECTION

The first anger exercise is "YES-NO." It will allow you to begin to feel the power of your anger.

Because anger is often internalized, start by going within. Close your eyes for a moment and internally identify a core issue that relates to feeling devalued, disrespected, etc. Write down your core issue. Take your time in order to clarify your core issue (such as abuse or a parent's alcoholism) versus focusing on issues pertaining to your job marriage, or other aspects of your life that have played out due to your core issue. Once you have written down your core issue, you are ready to move on.

First, write words that finish the statement related to your core issue. When listing YES statements, you are making proclamations of your value, strength, and power. Here are some examples:

- YES, you will respect me!

- YES, I have rights!

- YES, I will be heard!

- YES, I am important and powerful!

What do you need to say YES to? List them below:

YES, _____

YES, _____

YES, _____

YES, _____

YES, _____

Now consider the other side—NO. When listing NO statements, you are making declarations of your personal, emotional, and physical safety and boundaries. Here are some examples:

- NO, you won't abuse me!

- NO, you won't speak for me!

- NO, you won't tell me what to do!

- NO, I won't cower down to you!

What do you need to say NO to? List them below:

NO, _____

NO, _____

NO, _____

NO, _____

NO, _____

Next, take a moment to recenter yourself. Close your eyes again and reflect on the phrases "I WANT IT" and "YOU CAN'T HAVE IT." Internally focus on your core issue and what each phrase empowers you to think. As thoughts and feelings emerge regarding your core issue, write them down as well.

See what the "I WANT IT" statement may reveal. Here are some examples:

- I want my freedom!

- I want to be in charge of my body!

- I want my power!

- I want to be heard!

what do you WANT? List them below:

I WANT _____

I WANT _____

I WANT _____

I WANT _____

I WANT _____

The "YOU CAN'T HAVE IT" may exemplify:

- You can't have control!

- You can't have my body!

- You can't have my sanity!

- You can't have power over me anymore!

what belongs to you that NO ONE can have? List those things below:

YOU CAN'T HAVE _____

YOU CAN'T HAVE _____

YOU CAN'T HAVE _____

YOU CAN'T HAVE _____

YOU CAN'T HAVE _____

Oftentimes in life, women are told that their thoughts, feelings and beliefs are wrong, and that the other person is right. Finish writing about the ways your thoughts, feelings and beliefs have been right. It's a validation and declaration of self-esteem!

● I'M RIGHT

_____

_____

● YOU'RE WRONG!

_____

_____

Often, women take this writing and reflection to the next level. After completing your writing, you will likely feel a renewed sense of personal power. New insights and awareness can truly be liberating. Although it is quite simple, there are several steps to take in order to physically experience this newfound energy.

Give yourself the opportunity to experience this exercise more fully. The primary goal is for you to physically and emotionally feel the power of the words you have written. You will need the following:

● a safe person (such as a close friend, trusted spouse/partner, family member, or counselor) who is not afraid of intense expression of emotion

● a safe place where you can get as loud as you need to be

● drinking water

● tissues

● perhaps a cushion or pillow or something to punch

Your safe person needs to be someone who is willing to be your partner in a volume exercise, which will require her or him to also yell loudly. Begin by asking your safe person to stand face-to-face across from you. Some women place a piece of tape on the floor between themselves and their partner to visually represent a safety line. Remember that your anger is normal and necessary and is not meant to be destructive. Also, remember that as you get loud with your safe person, you are not yelling "at" that person. Your partner for this exercise is providing containment as you find your voice and your power.

As you face each other, be certain to stand solidly on the floor with your feet shoulder-width apart. Ask your partner to push on your shoulders to make sure you are not a "pushover." If you are, replant your feet so you are standing firm.

With your arms uncrossed, both of you are to look into the left eye of the other—the left eye is said to be the "window to the soul." This helps both of you to get grounded and to know that your partner is supporting you through this exercise, and you are doing the same in return.

Review your written list and then close your eyes as you visualize your core issue. Although your partner has likely not written a list, she or he can gain more benefit to also close her or his eyes and connect with a core issue as well. Based on your comfort level, you may choose to state your core issue out loud to your partner, or just keep it safe within yourself. Once you are clear about your core issue, you are ready to begin. Decide if you want to start with the word "YES" or "NO." Throughout the exercise, your partner will match your volume, answering only with the opposite word.

Once you begin, you will say only one word, YES or NO! This allows you to stay focused and clear, and to feel and hear your own power. Each time the "YES-NO" is exchanged, the "YES" increases in volume. The "NO" responds at the same level, though not getting louder or overpowering the "YES." It is similar to watching children arguing, "YES"-"NO," and on and on again. The person who will be saying "YES" starts.

It is very common to find that you are unable to get loud at first. Think about two children arguing to visualize the intensity that is possible. Give yourself permission to get as loud as you can—allow yourself to "raise the top off the roof." Another typical response you may notice is that you or your partner smile or become tearful and cry. Know that this is natural, but work hard not to smile, as it can diminish your power. Also, work hard to "push beyond your tears," as tears can reduce the power or strength of the message you are trying to convey. Your partner may also need to signal you with a thumbs-up to encourage you to raise your volume and get louder. If your voice is coming from your throat, you will cough and may feel like you are choking. If that happens, place your hand on your abdomen and bring your volume up from your diaphragm, not your throat. You may also find it helpful to allow a guttural or primal sound to emerge from your body.

As the exercise continues, and you both become louder and more comfortable with your word, then switch. If you had been saying "YES," it is now your turn to say "NO." You may focus on the same core issue, or you may find that a deeper one may have emerged during the process. The exercise starts again with the new "YES" person beginning the process. Naturally, the energy and intensity will die down and you both will stop. In between exchanges, you may begin coughing or gagging, so take a drink in between exercises.

The experience continues with the next phrase that you wrote about. Review your list, close your eyes to center yourself on the words you wrote, and then choose which phrase you would like to start with:

- I WANT IT!

- YOU CAN'T HAVE IT!

Again, as you find the energy and intensity naturally dying down, stop, change phrases, and start again. Take drinks of water in between rotations as needed.

Repeat the same steps outlined above for the next phrases:

- I'M RIGHT!

- YOU'RE WRONG!

We teach women that physically externalizing depression and sadness allows them to transform them into energy. Our belief is that depression and sadness are often the result of unexpressed anger. When physically released, the anger is more useful. Anger is an energizing agent due to the adrenaline it produces. When women feel energy and adrenaline rushing through their bodies, they can mobilize their lives differently and accomplish personal goals that are empowering and life-changing.

Once you have expressed and externalized your anger, you will be more likely to discard it and detach from it, which allows you to move into the forgiveness stage of letting go of anger. This does not necessarily mean that you forgive your perpetrator, but it means you no longer allow the anger to hold you back from being the person you want to be or from accomplishing the things you envision for your life.

When you liberate yourself from your feelings of anger, you naturally move into a forgiveness state. Only you can decide how and when you will do that. We believe that the process you create will be exactly what you need to take you on your journey of self-discovery and healing.

RACKETS AND PILLOWS: EXTERNALIZE THE ENERGY

Typically, after doing a YES-NO exercise, you may want to "physicalize" your work. This is a way for you to literally and physically connect with your power.

THE PROCESS

We ask you to kneel down in front of two or three stacked overstuffed pillows. For safety purposes, remove any rings or other jewelry.

Focus on a core issue that has created a trauma, injustice, or betrayal in your past. Common themes include sexual abuse, parental abandonment, divorce, disrespectful children, authoritative employers, chemical dependency, etc. As difficult as it may be to conceive, this exercise will liberate you from the power that others have had "over you." This allows you to recognize the powerful force your anger has been for you. Unfortunately, your anger has most likely locked you into your feelings as opposed to releasing them. When you externalize the anger, you are no longer limited by internalized fear, and you automatically take charge of your life with confidence and assuredness.

When you beat on the pillows with a tennis racket as hard and as loud as you can, you become increasingly in touch with the surging energy moving through your body. We also would encourage you to use a word that speaks directly about your anger. Some women groan, growl, curse, or speak short sentences (such as "I hate you! You are a bastard!").

Although some women can externalize their anger in five minutes or less, you should beat the pillows until you are completely spent, with no energy left. After you feel like you have no more energy left within you, we would ask you to beat the pillows ten more times to push beyond the fatigue. Oftentimes, this is the most powerful part of the exercise because you utilize stored-up energy that has been inaccessible for years.

When you are finally done, you may even have blisters on your hands, symbolizing the work you did. Repeated anger work may result in your being fortunate enough to have destroyed your pillow with the innards coming out—if so, tell yourself that these innards are the "guts" of your anger and keep a part of them to remind you that you have externalized and released your anger.

PROCESS THE WORK

After you have completed your work and before you retire for the evening, answer the following questions:

where in your body do you feel energy?

_____

_____

_____

what color is the energy?

_____

what adjective best describes how you feel at this moment?

_____

_____

_____

This is a type of anchoring that has its roots in Neurolinguistic Programming (NLP) and is helpful in anchoring and honoring the processing that you have done.

INTEGRATION

Write a short paragraph describing your experience. This work will create a shift in you, so we recommend that you write several times this week about how your life is different now that you have released the anger. You may be extremely sore physically and emotionally raw, so it is critical for you to set up some self-care behaviors in this next week.

Releasing the anger has...

_____

_____

_____

The thoughts I have after doing the exercise are...

_____

_____

_____

I feel stronger now that I have done the exercise because...

_____

_____

_____

I will practice self-care by...

_____

_____

_____

ALTERNATIVES TO RACKET WORK

If you have a physical limitation that prevents you from doing racket work, you can tear up old books or catalogues instead. As you rip the pages, verbalize your feelings and then rip through more pages. It takes great strength and energy to tear fifteen, twenty, or thirty pages at one time. The sound of the pages ripping, combined with the power such action requires, provides a therapeutic way to release pent-up aggression.

You may find alternatives that are safe such as smashing clay to be highly effective also. In some communities, such as ours, women can visit "Wreck-a-Room" to externalize their anger.

VESUVIUS: EXTERNALIZATION OF ANGER AND DEVELOPMENT OF PERSONAL BOUNDARIES

You need a trusted friend as a support person for this exercise. "Vesuvius" is an exercise that was initially developed for couples. It has been adapted from PAIRS, a couples program that has been around for decades. We have found it to be a tremendous exercise for a woman, because it allows you to release your anger and experience support from a friend whom you have asked to assist you in this exercise.

This exercise also encourages you to get in touch with suppressed or repressed anger. Women are often taught that they should not have ugly, angry thoughts and feelings. Not only will you get to spew your feelings, but you will get some interrupted time to say whatever is locked inside of you. This exercise gives women permission to identify their feelings and to erupt like the ancient volcano, Vesuvius.

> THIS EXERCISE IS FOR YOU IF YOU ARE REALLY, REALLY ANGRY!

PURPOSE OF THE VESUVIUS

This ritual allows for the emotional purging and spewing that needs to occur when your anger has been suppressed and repressed for years or even decades. If you are tired, frustrated, and enraged, you will find this tool a safe way to unload, uncork, and explode. It is done with permission and for an allotted amount of time. The following steps outline the Vesuvius process.

THE PROCESS

1. You request a certain amount of time to vent your anger, frustration, and rage. In most cases, this exercise requires three, five, or ten minutes. (You will likely find that when you have uninterrupted time to say what is really on your mind, you will be quite direct and focused on what you have to say, and you typically won't need a huge amount of time.) Your friend will stand in front of you and will silently be a witness to your anger. This person is called the "container," because she or he metaphorically holds your anger. This person also serves as the timekeeper and tells you when your time to vent is up.

2. Your friend will be learning and practicing how to contain your anger without internalizing it. She or he is asked to visualize a Plexiglass shield, a Teflon coating, a wall, or any other protective mechanism that allows her or him to avoid internalizing your anger that is spewing forth. She or he may want to internally speak a mantra such as, "This is not about me."

3. You begin by verbalizing your anger regarding a core issue. Here you emote your dark, ugly, and judgmental feelings. Nothing you say during this period has to be true, fair, or politically correct. Yelling and screaming is common, expected, and encouraged. Many times, as you share your anger, your issue will deepen, or your focus will shift to another person to whom the anger is directed. Many women have experienced that as they are yelling, their anger shifted from their husband or boss to their mother or father.

4. Once you have emotionally purged or after time has run out, you thank your friend for safely containing your anger. Then, it is vital to "de-role," acknowledging that your friend is not "your mother or father or husband," but rather my "friend who contained my anger and kept my confidence." Your friend then uses reflective listening to acknowledge that "I know I am not your mother, father, or husband, but I am (name), your friend."

5. After you and your friend debrief, you can share with each other what it was like to be in this exercise.

Survivors of sexual abuse or other forms of trauma often find this exercise frightening, yet freeing, because they can say whatever they want to the perpetrator(s), no matter how violent. Remember, if you are the listening friend during this exercise, you are not there to console or shut down the intense feelings. You are there as a neutral person to "contain them"...nothing more and nothing less!

SEXUAL ABUSE AND OTHER TRAUMAS

Three out of ten women report experiencing childhood sexual abuse. Consequently, you may have experienced a trauma that is blocking you from being everything you can be. For this reason, it is imperative that you address any trauma and trust issues that stem from this abuse and neglect. Exercises that focus on empowerment provide the strength necessary to help you move from victimization to survivorship.

Processing pain is good for the soul!

Bad things happen to good people all the time. It is likely that as you grew up, some unfortunate things happened to you. Enlightened people will want to work on processing these events so they can understand them better and grow from them. That is truly one aspect of living a good life. When trauma occurs, it is so very important to acknowledge the feelings and work through the pain so that you can make sense of your world and redirect your life in a purposeful way.

We work with numerous women who have experienced trauma. In many cases, the initial trauma occurred in their childhood and they did not have the support or resources to help them resolve it as it was happening or directly afterward. The trauma might have been from living with an alcoholic parent; being physically, emotionally, or sexually abused; or living in chronic poverty. If women aren't given the opportunity to process and work through their trauma, there is high likelihood that they will re-experience it as an adult. Until it is understood and resolved in one's own psyche, the trauma will return again and again until she can figure it out and truly reprocess it. Once she has worked through the issues, she will undoubtedly feel stronger, healthier, and better able to use the skills she learned from resolving the trauma to improve her life. This means that she also has to go through the process of forgiveness because forgiveness allows her to let the trauma go and move on. It is the process of letting go that will allow and encourage her to find meaningful ways of growing and contributing to life so that she feels good about herself.

If this experience is bringing up deep emotional wounds, we highly recommend that you process your work with a trauma specialist.

All the great theorists say that it is the suffering that promotes human beings to grow into people who are fully actualized and evolved. Many of you may be saying, "why do we need to experience so much suffering to actualize growth?" what we believe to be true is that life does have much purpose and if one does not deal with the past pains, one cannot learn and get healthier. If you don't work through the pain, you will likely stay stuck and blocked from allowing good things to come into your life. As therapists, we are saddened to watch clients repeatedly experience hardships, and yet the work they do to work through the blocks makes them stronger, wiser, and more self-actualized!

TIME FOR REFLECTION

what pain from your childhood continues to haunt you?

How do you believe that this experience or trauma has blocked you from growing?

How has it shown up in your life again in a different way?

How have you sought out support and resources to help you work through pain?

How has your suffering made you stronger?

*List how you have grown and/or
identify the ways in which you want to grow.*

If you have been trying to do this work on your own, you have more than likely felt alone because of the trauma that occurred in your past. If this is the case, we strongly encourage you to seek out support and resources to help you work through the pain. Both individual and group therapy provide much opportunity to access support in your life.

You deserve to get healthy and release yourself from the pain. Get some help so that you can heal and use your past to strengthen the future!

Now, let's move on to other exercises to acknowledge the pain and make you stronger.

Letters

In therapy, women are routinely asked to write a letter, role-play, or create a script or play to re-enact the trauma, and then create an ending or resolution piece that empowers them and allows them to put to rest the long-standing issues. These writing exercises draw much wisdom from Narrative Therapy.

Your writing may not be the reality of the situation, but when issues are acted out, the old brain/primal brain does not know the difference, and some resolution or peace can be achieved.

If you choose to write a letter, consider writing two letters of a different nature: (1) an irrational, angry, hostile, ugly letter, where you will bring up all of the hateful, resentful and vengeful thoughts that you may have had your entire life; and (2) a letter that serves to reclaim your survivorship and move beyond being a victim.

LETTER 1: THE VENOMOUS LETTER

After describing the trauma and its effects, you are encouraged to be vengeful and to let your "shadow side" take over. You may tell the perpetrator that you want to chop off his penis, or that you hope he dies lonely and isolated, or that you hope he gets cancer and it eats away at his body. The important thing is to acknowledge all of the thoughts and feelings that you have had in the past for cathartic purposes. Our experience is that catharsis is extremely beneficial in resolving sexual abuse and does not promote violence. Again, this is a very liberating experience, releasing the pent-up feelings you have been feeling your whole life.

LETTER 2: THE SURVIVOR LETTER

The second letter is a rational, direct, assertive letter telling the perpetrator your feelings and the consequences of his or her actions. This helps to reclaim your strength and to move on from the event. Finishing with the rational letter helps you to reclaim yourself as a strong survivor and helps to provide closure. It further allows you an extra opportunity to regain composure.

Therefore, it is always necessary to finish this activity with the second letter!

Tell Your Story

WRITE YOUR SCRIPT OR PLAY

Sometimes it is helpful to write a play or dialogue to re-enact the trauma and then create a preferred ending or resolution piece that empowers you and allows you to begin to put to rest the long-standing issue. Some women spend several weeks doing this, finding themselves blocked to this process. If you get stuck in this way, we suggest connecting with a good friend who is skilled at writing and willing to co-write it with you. Such a friend can offer a fresh perspective that helps you script out the piece together. She or he will also validate your experience and normalize your feelings. Working with a friend will both help you complete your script and provide you with extra support. Through this experience, you may develop a bond with your friend that further deepens your relationship! Not only is it cathartic that you can create a script or play about the wrongs of the trauma, but you also increase your sense of trust with your friend, which may have been one of the primary experiences you lost as a child.

CONFLICT: A NEW PERSPECTIVE

Conflict can be difficult. Most people were not taught how to handle conflict effectively, and so it can evoke lots of uncomfortable feelings. You are most likely either someone who avoids it at all costs or someone who goes for the jugular so you can "get them before they can get you." Oftentimes in therapy, we teach people to practice assertiveness when they are angry with others, working through ways that they can share their feelings, thoughts, and beliefs with clarity. Being assertive does not mean that they get what they want, only that they can be sure they were clear and direct about their feelings related to the conflict. Often, a tougher situation arises when you know someone is angry with you, but you are not sure how to approach the situation to resolve or work through the issues.

"OWNING OUR STORY CAN BE HARD BUT NOT NEARLY AS DIFFICULT AS SPENDING OUR LIVES RUNNING FROM IT." – BRENÉ BROWN

FEAR OF CONFLICT EXERCISES

What we know to be true is that women have been taught to suppress conflict. By and large, women are not socialized to externalize anger. Most women either internalize the conflict and ignore it, or become frustrated by it and act out. Women are not usually taught to express it directly.

The following exercises provide a way to practice the skills of sharing conflict and not personalizing it. Freud theorized that 90 percent of all conflict is projection, meaning that most conflict is usually about the other person.

What have you been taught about conflict?

_____

_____

_____

_____

_____

More than likely, you were not taught how to assert yourself and deal with conflict directly and honestly.

How did your parents role model conflict for you?

_____

_____

_____

_____

_____

Both of us have made it our personal mission to teach women how not to avoid conflict, but to recognize that it is normal, natural, and necessary ... and, in healthy relationships, working through conflict will build intimacy. If you are dealing with someone terribly dysfunctional or unhealthy, then handling conflict without personalizing it will keep you from taking it on and feeling like you are responsible for someone else's feelings.

THE FOUR TOOLS OF CONFLICT

The conflict model that we will be talking about has some very unusual components and will need to be practiced in order for you to get comfortable with this approach. The model entails working through four steps.

When someone is angry with you, recognize the person's criticism and ask yourself the following questions:

1. How did I contribute to this conflict? Recognize your involvement and remind yourself that you did indeed contribute to the problem, however, tell yourself that you will only own 10 percent of the conflict. Validate what you did and assure the other person that you won't make the same mistake again.

2. Now remember that 90 percent of the conflict is typically about the other person. In other words, the sender of the conflict is struggling with something and is projecting it onto you. Therefore, it is important to recognize that this person's need to put you down, argue with you, or be critical of you comes out of an unresolved issue within him or her. You then tell yourself, "This is not about me; this is about the other person." Say it over and over to yourself (silently, of course).

3. Tell yourself that you are not going to let the other person's anger get to you. You may even want to say, "I won't give him or her the power to make me feel _____ (a feeling word like disrespected, angry, or inferior).

4. The last step is to reinforce that you have faith in one of three ways: (1) That you are strong enough to weather the conflict, which

reinforces your resilience; (2) faith that you and the person in conflict will resolve the issues. This will allow you to approach the person with a positive attitude. If the person refuses to forgive you or work with you, then you must recognize again that this is HIS or HER issue; or (3), you can have the faith in a higher power and surrender the conflict to that power, whether that is God or the Universe or your Higher Power. Know that surrendering means that it will ultimately get worked out. This allows you to depersonalize the conflict and no longer be affected by it. It also reminds you that there is something greater than you who can support you through these tough times.

IMAGINE THESE SCENARIOS:

Have you ever had a fight with your spouse where hurtful and unfair things were said? Later, your spouse apologized and said, "I didn't really mean those things." If you had used this new approach regarding the conflict, you would have not personalized the situation. Once the argument was over, you could have calmly decided what useful information you were able to gain without feeling personally wounded by the verbal attack.

Using the 4-step model deflates the power behind the hurtful words.

Has your boss ever taken you aside and made statements that inferred that you were a disappointment as an employee? You are perplexed, because you are trying your hardest and doing your best.

Using this model means that you look for opportunities to improve your performance, but simultaneously realize that your boss may be under some pressure to get the employees to sell more or produce faster. This approach to conflict helps you to hear the evaluative remarks without allowing them to affect your self-esteem.

When you use this approach, you will walk out of the encounter with insight and with your self-esteem intact. When you refuse to take things personally, you are not as defensive. This allows you the gift of insight because you will know what you need to do to improve the situation. Conflict will no longer scare you. You won't take on the criticism.

Although using the concepts of this model may feel foreign to you at first, in time you will likely find that you become less afraid of conflict, which makes you more objective about its reality. This approach teaches you that all-important skill: not to take things so personally. It is like you are coated with Teflon! Look for opportunities to use this approach and notice how liberating it is to put the situation into perspective. Conflict will become a tool to understand the other person better, which helps in the relationship-building process.

"IT TOOK ME QUITE A LONG TIME TO DEVELOP A VOICE, AND NOW THAT I HAVE IT, I AM NOT GOING TO BE SILENT."
— MADELEINE ALBRIGHT

Assertiveness: Develop Your Communication Backbone

We work with people from all types of backgrounds and lifestyles, and consistently see one commonality, especially among women. Women come into the office, they often lack the ability to assert themselves with others. Most women don't know what assertiveness is, let alone know how to do it. If they do know how to do it, it is because they have seen an important person in their life assert him or herself on a regular basis.

Assertiveness means standing up for your beliefs. It is being clear about what you think and how you feel. When you are assertive, you let others know the real you, and you stay true to yourself so that you can achieve your goals and move closer to what you need. Assertiveness is conveying a direct message about your needs. It is proactive, and it empowers you to change.

What is your personal definition of assertiveness?

_____

_____

_____

_____

If you want to have better self-esteem and get your needs met, you must learn how to assert yourself. we call it developing your backbone—the backbone of self-esteem.

which person are you?

- Do you assert yourself with others?

- Do people know how you feel and what you think?

- Do you speak about what is on your mind in a direct, concise manner?

- Do people know the real you and what you stand for?

- Do you ask for what you want/need?

or:

- Are you afraid to share feelings for fear of hurting others?

- Do you squelch your opinions because you think they aren't important, or you are afraid they will be shot down?

- Are you afraid to speak your mind, because if you are, your needs may not be getting met and you will feel that double rejection?

- Do you suppress your own needs to please others?

which person are you? It's important to be honest so that you can make the needed change. Are you the first one or the second one?

Most women have never received any formal assertiveness training. This workbook will help you to polish your assertiveness skills.

Oftentimes women who don't assert themselves get walked on or they find themselves putting their needs on the back burner. Assertiveness keeps you out of the victim role. It lets people know where you stand. Many life strategists stress that you teach people how to treat you. When you assert yourself, you teach others about your feelings, limits, and boundaries. You no longer can get walked on because you have changed your behavior.

There are two basic formulas you can use to assert yourself. Both involve using "I" messages. Begin by thinking about something you have kept to yourself, and then practice using one of these sentences to share your thoughts. Take a moment now to fill in the blanks:

ASSERTIVENESS STATEMENTS

1. _____ , when you _____
   (person's name)   *(behavior)*

   I feel _____ because _____
   (feeling word)   *(the message it sends me, or the message I hear is)*

   _____

2. I don't like _____ , and this is what I'm
   (the behavior)

   going to do about it if it occurs again _____
   (statement of action you will take)

HERE ARE SOME EXAMPLES OF ASSERTIVENESS:

A young teen in a divorced family hears her mother saying bad things about her father. She says, "Mom, when you say that Dad doesn't care about us, it makes me feel sad because the message I hear is that I am unlovable."

The newlywed tells her husband, "When you tease me about my failed attempts at taking care of the house, I feel angry because what I hear is, I'm not a good wife."

The mother of three who tells her alcoholic husband, "I am no longer going to allow you to treat me that way. The next time it happens, I will leave the room, ask you to leave, and go to a support group for people with alcoholic husbands."

The important thing to remember about assertiveness is that it is about you. It is not used to change others. Many women complain that their assertiveness will not get their husband or another person to change. That is exactly right—being assertive is simply about letting another person know how their behavior affects you, which puts you one step closer to you changing yourself. Being assertive does not guarantee that the other person will hear you; but it does mean that you are being strong and direct about how you think and feel. The exciting part of assertiveness is that once you are clear with others, you will feel better about yourself Consequently, you work on doing things that will move you closer to getting your needs met.

USING THE ASSERTIVENESS FORMULA

As an experiment, think of one thing that had to do with your feelings that you have kept inside and not shared with others. Using the assertiveness formula, practice filling in the blanks and imagine yourself saying that statement to the other person. Be sure to actually write the statement down, which will make you more likely to use it in your daily life. It takes practice, but we guarantee that the more you practice it, the easier it will be to create and use assertiveness statements. When you concentrate on changing yourself and not others, you speed the process of getting what you want and need. After all, practice makes permanent!

1. _____ , when you _____
   (person's name)   *(behavior)*

   I feel _____ because _____
         (feeling word)   *(the message it sends me, or the message I hear is)*

   _____

2. I don't like _____ , and this is what I'm
               (the behavior)

   going to do about it if it occurs again _____
                              (statement of action you will take)

   _____

1. [_____] , when you _____
      (person's name)   (behavior)

   I feel _____ because _____
              (feeling word)   (the message it sends me, or the message I hear is)

   _____

2. I don't like _____ , and this is what I'm
                          (the behavior)

   going to do about it if it occurs again _____
                                          (statement of action you will take)

---

1. [_____] , when you _____
      (person's name)   (behavior)

   I feel _____ because _____
              (feeling word)   (the message it sends me, or the message I hear is)

   _____

2. I don't like _____ , and this is what I'm
                          (the behavior)

   going to do about it if it occurs again _____
                                          (statement of action you will take)

   _____

1. _____, when you _____
        (person's name)   *(behavior)*

I feel _____ because _____
        (feeling word)   *(the message it sends me, or the message I hear is)*

_____

2. I don't like _____, and this is what I'm
                              (the behavior)

going to do about it if it occurs again _____
                                      (statement of action you will take)

_____

---

1. _____, when you _____
        (person's name)   *(behavior)*

I feel _____ because _____
        (feeling word)   *(the message it sends me, or the message I hear is)*

_____

2. I don't like _____, and this is what I'm
                              (the behavior)

going to do about it if it occurs again _____
                                      (statement of action you will take)

_____

TRUST EXERCISES

Trust comes from being honest even in the face of conflict. Honest expression of emotions can create conflict, making it challenging to be assertive. There may be people in your life who will not allow you to be assertive, and may attack you for it. Therefore, it is necessary to assess how emotionally safe a situation may be. We have met many women whose trust was violated as a child or may be in a volatile relationship. As a result, they did not allow themselves to trust easily, or ever again. In these cases, it becomes important to limit your exposure to them in order to be able to fully express yourself, and surround yourself with those whom you can trust to accept and validate your emotions.

Answer the following questions to assess your "trustability."

Are you someone who has trouble trusting others? If so, why?

_____

_____

_____

_____

_____

_____

List previous experiences that have seriously affected your ability to trust.

Experience 1.

_____

_____

_____

_____

_____

_____

Experience 2.

_____

_____

_____

_____

_____

_____

Experience 3.

_____

_____

_____

_____

_____

_____

Experience 4.

_____

_____

_____

_____

_____

_____

what enables you to trust others?

_____

_____

_____

_____

_____

_____

Perhaps you pick people who treat you kindly, or who sit next to you at family functions, or who have something in common with you, like having an alcoholic father.

It is important to use your intuition and life experiences. As Dr. Maya Angelou said, "when people show you who they are, believe them the first time." This means it is YOUR responsibility to protect yourself from people who consistently hurt you.

Are there people in your life who have consistently hurt you? If so, who are those people? write their names below and explain why you continue to allow this to happen.

REASON FOR ALLOWING THE PATTERN OF ABUSE

Person 1: _____ — _____
          Name   *Pattern of Abuse/Mistreatment*

Person 2: _____ — _____
          Name   *Pattern of Abuse/Mistreatment*

Person 3: _____ — _____
          Name   *Pattern of Abuse/Mistreatment*

This workbook is designed to help you see patterns that you want to break. Sometimes you'll need the help of a good therapist to change unhealthy patterns, especially if you find yourself consistently allowing others to hurt or take advantage of you. If you have had a lot of trauma in your life, seek out a therapist with specialized trauma training.

Women need to feel safety, connection, and trust. Continue to work on ways of finding safe people whom you can form a healthy connection with to develop ongoing trust. If you have gotten this far in your workbook...we know you are making great progress! Building safety, connection, and trust takes a long time, so notice your progress and keep the faith that as you grow healthier, so will your relationships!

9. Mind & Body Tools

"YOU ARE THE ONE THAT POSSESSES THE KEYS TO YOUR BEING.
YOU CARRY THE PASSPORT TO YOUR OWN HAPPINESS."
– DIANE VON FURSTENBERG.

Cognitive Behavioral Exercises: The Chart Method

Individuals in recovery track their sobriety time. They know the last time they used alcohol or drugs, and they know that their first day clean is their sobriety date – they can tell you they have 30 days clean or 72 days clean or 3 ½ years clean. Charting progress is helpful so you can see all the work you have done and how it has paid off in your life. We find cognitive behavioral therapy (CBT) to be extremely valuable as a concrete way to keep track of your progress. CBT creates change by allowing us to question and examine our thoughts, which produces alternate ways of thinking, thus reinforcing new healthy behaviors. We recommend using a chart to hold yourself accountable for working on your goals.

Visual cues serve as a reminder of our accomplishments. A chart allows you to clearly see your success or lack thereof regarding your goal. A visual reminder is an extra reminder to hold you accountable.

Give yourself the assignment to list on a poster board how many times you have demonstrated a new behavior. One woman tracked her DWC days, which were her "days without cutting." One woman knew she always attracted unhealthy men and vowed to stay out of unhealthy relationships, so she tracked her DWR days, "days without relationship."

Here are some of the new behaviors you may want to keep track of:

- How many times have you practiced assertiveness?

- How many times have you created boundaries and said no?

- How many times have you not been self-destructive?

- How many times have you not binged or purged?

- How many times have you not called your ex-husband?

- How many social contacts have you made in a week?

The Chart Method increases individual accountability. It not only serves as a concrete vehicle to map out your success, but it also acts as a visual reminder of progress or relapse.

Change How You See Yourself: Body Image Exercises

Body distortion is common among women. We strive to help women accept their bodies just as they are, regardless of their size or weight. Shame about our bodies only serves to reinforce a negative self-image, and this makes change more difficult. Oftentimes, there has been past trauma that has contributed to negative body image. The body image exercise will assist you in identifying past traumas.

BODY IMAGE DRAWING

This can be an emotional exercise and may be best to do with your friend, sponsor, therapist, or coach for extra safety.

Perhaps some trauma has occurred in your life that has greatly impacted your body image. If you would like to assess whether this may be at the core of your inability to "like your body," the following exercise can be helpful to uncover your feelings.

Buy some large newsprint paper from an office supply store and ask a friend to come over and draw the entire outline of your body. You do this by laying on your back or taping it on a wall so you can stand in front of the paper. After you have the outline, draw symbols or choose pictures or words from a magazine that epitomize your self-image, body image, and stories that contribute to your sense of self. You may also draw pictures around or outside of the outline to identify past issues, fears, or events.

Here are some common areas that you may choose to depict:

- the genitals, which may be blacked out with an X because of sexual trauma

- your eyes may be taped shut from seeing physical abuse

- no mouths because of having no voice as a child, no power to speak

- empty faces because it felt like you had no identity

- broken hearts because of relationships ending

- babies that may have been aborted or miscarried

After you complete the drawing portion of this exercise, it can be helpful to write about your feelings. Doing so can be cathartic and can help you better understand how someone may have betrayed you and how this has played out in your body. If this exercise feels too disturbing, then it is important to call your therapist so you can process it together.

This exercise can be one of the toughest to do because our bodies have carried the shame of trauma, cultural bias, manipulation, and sexual indoctrination. The body keeps score of the pain and trauma that has been inflicted on you. In addition, societal pressure has laid a lot of pressure on women to conform to the genre of the day. This may have caused you to want to change your appearance to conform to "the standards and mores of the day.". We have been so culturally brainwashed to believe that our bodies should be seen in a certain way. We are not taught to appreciate our bodies because of the strength that our bodies posses to move us forward in life.

CREATE A CUSTOMIZED PLAN FOR TAKING BETTER CARE OF YOUR BODY

When you are working on improving your body image, it is important to see your body in a new way while you are working on your goals. The first thing we ask you to do is to look at your body as a friend. It is important to acknowledge how your body has served you and to appreciate it exactly as it is so that you will create a gentle plan for improving it.

Do you have a goal for your body? Instead of being critical, are you able to identify what you like about your body? We encourage you to use the technique of "reframing." Reframing is an important life skill because it encourages you to look at things differently. For example, instead of thinking, "I'm huge" or "I'm fat," you tell yourself that you are voluptuous, soft, or curvaceous. This mindset promotes self-love, which in turn promotes self-care. After all, language shapes attitude, and gentler words result in a gentler view of self. Then you are more likely to change if you like yourself.

Now that you have the proper mindset, let's get down to business. What changes would you like to make to obtain a healthier body? Write down one or two specific things you would like to accomplish and, as you do, keep the following in mind:

Be realistic. We see so many women who want to "weigh the same weight" as when they got married twenty years ago. We would discourage you from picking a weight and suggest that you focus on something other than a number.

Think differently. Use a different word to describe your goal. Do you want to be more physically fit, more muscular, healthier, or smaller?

Create a plan that supports the goal. You will be more successful when you think about your goals in small increments. "I will lose one to two pounds this week" or "I would like to fit into my size 14 jeans (instead of the 16's) within twenty-one days." This type of goal can typically be accomplished in a shorter amount of time. Plus, it reinforces positive behavioral changes, making it more likely that you will stick to your goals.

Take steps to cut out one unhealthy behavior and keep practicing it. Work on this repeatedly, and as you see consistent progress it will become part of your daily routine and no longer need to think about it. It will become automatic.

For many women, this means they stop eating after six or six o'clock, or they stay away from the vending machines at work. Instead of eliminating something, you may need to add something in order to support your goal. Towards weight loss, find a friend who also wants to get in shape and make weekly exercise dates to get together and support each other in eating healthier and working out.

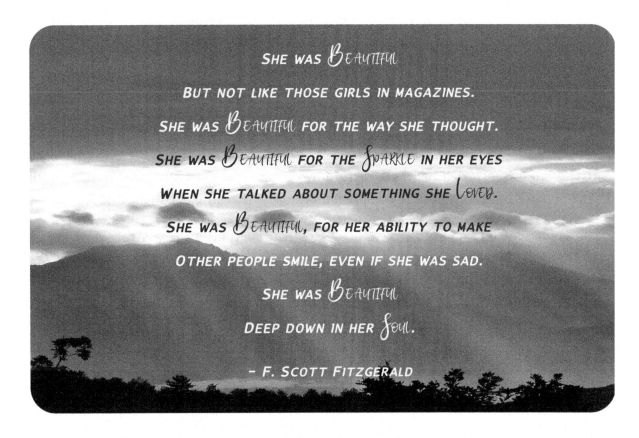

SHE WAS *Beautiful*

BUT NOT LIKE THOSE GIRLS IN MAGAZINES.

SHE WAS *Beautiful* FOR THE WAY SHE THOUGHT.

SHE WAS *Beautiful* FOR THE *Sparkle* IN HER EYES

WHEN SHE TALKED ABOUT SOMETHING SHE *Loved.*

SHE WAS *Beautiful*, FOR HER ABILITY TO MAKE

OTHER PEOPLE SMILE, EVEN IF SHE WAS SAD.

SHE WAS *Beautiful*

DEEP DOWN IN HER *Soul.*

– F. SCOTT FITZGERALD

REPLACE OLD BEHAVIORS WITH NEW ONES

Focus on creating healthy behaviors so you do not experience a sense of deprivation. You will lose weight if you...

- drink eight to ten glasses of water each day

- walk for twenty minutes daily

- stop eating after seven o'clock in the evening

- eat more vegetables

- gain more muscle

- develop a new hobby that takes up "grazing time"

It is important to focus on healthy behaviors to achieve your goals. When you choose the behaviors, you pick the consequences. That translates into direct actions:

- When I choose to walk twenty minutes per day, I speed up my metabolism.

- When I choose to write down what I eat, I consume fewer calories.

At the end of each day or week, write down your successes. Reaching a goal requires that you take notice of your accomplishments on the way toward that goal.

The guidelines you have just read are life strategies. Creating a strategy that works for you is thought provoking and exciting. You will need to integrate these strategies into your daily routine to maintain a healthy lifestyle. As you put together your very own customized plan, remember to pick behaviors that you can practice not just for today, but for the rest of your life.

In his book, *Just One Thing*, Rick Hanson highlights the need to do just one thing, and he starts with "Be Good to Yourself." Start by identifying just one goal to take better care of yourself.

The goal that I would like to work on is...

_____

_____

_____

_____

_____

My new healthy behavior will be...

_____

_____

_____

_____

_____

Some things that I am doing right are...

_____

_____

_____

_____

_____

One positive aspect of my problem/concern/issue is...

_____

_____

_____

_____

One change I have made this week to get closer to my goal is...

_____

_____

_____

_____

_____

Change Your Thinking—and Your Metaphor

METAPHORS CAN HELP CHANGE YOUR LIFE

If you're having difficulty changing your internal dialogue, you may need to shift your thinking. One of the fastest ways to create change is to draw a picture or find an image of the problems that have affected your life.

Have you found yourself talking in metaphors about our situation? Do you hear yourself talking about "the garbage" or feeling at the "end of your rope?"

We have heard overcommitted women feel like "gerbils on a wheel." Women with chaos in their lives may view that they are "caught in a tornado." Women who struggle with bipolar disorder often identify life as "being on a roller coaster." Some women who do not attend to their own needs may describe their life as a rubber band being stretched to capacity, feeling as though they may snap. Depressed or suicidal women have viewed themselves in a coffin or buried in a cemetery.

Do you relate to any of these images? If so, would you be willing to draw that image, write about it, and then draw another image representing what you would prefer to believe about yourself?

When you speak in metaphors, it can anchor a picture in your subconscious that results in a sense of finality. We work from the presumption that these exercises are a vehicle to unlock your "stuckness." We believe that when you form a different picture, you will be developing a new neurocircuitry that creates a different mindset to catapult you into healthier thoughts and beliefs about yourself. When you change your thinking, the things around you change. Therefore, by utilizing new metaphors you tap into your unconscious and allow a solution to emerge in your conscious thought. The next pages guide you to reshape the negative metaphor which may be keeping you stuck.

CREATE A VISUAL IMAGE OF THE PROBLEM

As stated, women often speak in metaphors to describe a dilemma. They describe feeling immobilized and stuck in a particular situation. Creating a visual image helps them move beyond the identified problem. If we were to ask you to find ways to decrease your stress, it could add to the overload you already feel. However, when you create a visual image that is different from what you believe in your psyche, you will naturally come to "know" what to do to reduce or decrease stress.

NAME THE METAPHOR

Complete the following statements:

My life is like a...

_____

_____

_____

My depression/my anxiety can best be described as...

_____

_____

_____

DRAW THE METAPHOR

After you have described your metaphor, spend some time thinking about what that looks like and then draw a picture of it.

Next draw a picture of how you would like your life to be, as it relates to your metaphor. For example, you may draw a picture of the gerbil taking a rest from the wheel and eating or sleeping; you may depict the calm after the tornado storm; you may choose to illustrate yourself as the operator who controls the speed of the roller coaster, and on and on. The variations of imagery are endless.

Now notice how your metaphor has begun to shift in your life. Perhaps your tornado has lost its velocity; the coffin may no longer be nailed shut; or the rubber band is not stretched so far.

Your mind is extremely adept at creating change and helping you to get where you want to be, but you have to access it in new and different ways to create that change.

Congratulations on finishing up the experiential part of this workbook. Now it is time to proceed with your beliefs and thoughts which hold the key to moving beyond the obstacles and fears that can interfere with actualizing your potential.

IT IS TIME TO FACE YOUR FEARS

Now that you have done the hard personal work of processing your old beliefs that had about yourself, it is time to focus on what you really want in life and what may be holding you back.

WHAT FEARS CONTINUE TO HOLD YOU BACK?

Spend a few minutes in a quiet spot with your eyes closed and ask yourself:

what is stopping you from living out your life's plan or dream?

_____

_____

_____

_____

Could any of these fears be getting in your way:

- The fear of failure.

    o I have felt failure in the past when...

    _____

    _____

    _____

    _____

○ I believe it held me back because...

_____

_____

_____

_____

● The fear of embarrassment.

○ I am most embarrassed when...

_____

_____

_____

_____

● The fear of the unknown.

○ What I fear most is...

_____

_____

_____

_____

_____

● The fear of rejection.

○ If I become successful, I fear that I will be rejected because...

_____

_____

_____

_____

_____

- ● The fear of hurting others.

  - ○ If I achieve my goals, I am afraid that I will be hurting because it will make him or her feel

  _____

  _____

  _____

  _____

  _____

- ● The fear of success.

  - ○ If I were successful, I would fear...

  _____

  _____

  _____

  _____

  _____

If fear is holding you back, then it's time to face your fears head-on. We recommend that you share your fears openly and honestly with a family member, a mentor, or a friend you genuinely respect. Sometimes just talking about it unlocks the fear. If not, a therapist or life coach can help to get you past the stumbling blocks. If your fears are deeply rooted in your childhood or past pain, a therapist would be most appropriate. If your fear is about being unable to create a strategy to make it happen, a personal life coach can help you create that plan to move out of your comfort zone.

Don't let fear immobilize you from stretching and moving into that new comfort zone. We all know that you can't win unless you play. You absolutely have what it takes to move through this world with self-assuredness and confidence.

Live Your Life to the Fullest

We believe that you were born for *Greatness* and that you have heard "that whisper" which has encouraged you to pursue your passion and actualize your dreams.

Thinking in negatives creates obstacles that diffuse a person's possibilities.

It takes the same amount of energy to believe as it does to worry.

Make the choice to envision how you want your life to be, which results in an intentional belief in yourself!

HOW YOU SPEAK TO YOURSELF

Seeking to grow and expand into your potential requires positive thoughts. Developing the skill of positive self-talk is vital to good self-esteem, but it doesn't just happen. One must practice it diligently.

One of the essential concepts in personal life coaching is the belief that people are born for greatness. Marianne Williamson, author and spiritualist, gives us pause to consider, "Who am I to be brilliant, gorgeous, talented, fabulous...Actually, who are you not to be? Your playing small does not serve the world." Remember, you were born for greatness!

Dr. Wayne Dyer, in his book *The Power of Intention*, advocates that when we are in alignment with God, we can accomplish great things. To be able to implement our vision or mission in life requires a belief in our potential. He believes that our thoughts create a cause-and-effect relationship in the world. How many times have you said, "I'm not smart enough to pull that off" or "I don't have enough money to make that happen?" When you manifest these notions, you project energy that reinforces these negative thoughts, and you make them a reality.

Most people have only an inkling of what they are truly capable of. This is in part due to the negative messages they received as children, messages which are internalized and then repeated over and over as one developmentally progresses.

How would your confidence be affected if you participated in daily activities or exercises that primed you for greatness no matter what goals you were seeking?

For example, if you were a stay-at-home mother, imagine what would happen if you reminded yourself several times each day that you were investing in the most important commodity in the world when you decided to invest in human life—your children. How would your life be different as you moved through a normal routine if you told yourself that the resistance you met with your oldest was normal and natural and that staying the course assured your child that there were important boundaries in life that needed to be respected?

Or perhaps you are a person whose fears and anxieties keep you locked into the same old job or routine. Imagine what would happen if you spent a month, three months, or a year repeating statements that affirm your desire for a career change, or a move to a different part of the country. What if you said, "I am in the

TRANSFORMATIONS: A WOMAN'S JOURNEY TO SELF-DISCOVERY

process of discovering my perfect job," or "I am well suited to do a variety of things and believe that there are many opportunities waiting for me"? Would it motivate you to take the plunge and live life to its fullest?

People are masters at seeing obstacles that prevent them from living their dreams. They may say, "I could never move away and leave my extended family" or "I have too good a business to change locations" or "I won't be able to afford the move." Again, thinking in negatives creates obstacles that diffuse a person's possibilities. As the prolific author Richard Bach said, "Argue for your limitations, and sure enough, they're yours."

If that same person used positive self-talk, she might decide to act on her desire to live elsewhere by checking out the territory, job possibilities, and cost of living to create the reality she deserved!

CHANGING YOUR INTERNAL DIALOGUE

What is one area in which you lack confidence?

_____

_____

_____

_____

_____

_____

What are some ways that you can change your internal dialogue?

_____

_____

_____

_____

_____

_____

Each time you find yourself operating on negativity and scarcity, stop yourself. Restate the belief in positive terms.

_____

_____

_____

_____

_____

Make the commitment to change your internal dialogue for ninety days. Write out the positive changes that occur in your life during that period.

_____

_____

_____

_____

_____

How might journaling your positive changes make a difference in your life?

_____

_____

_____

_____

_____

WORDS SHAPE ATTITUDES: SPEAK CONFIDENTLY

When we teach seminars on improving self-esteem and self-confidence, we are frequently asked, "what is the number one way to convey a sense of confidence?" One of the most empowering things a person can do is to speak confidently and with authority. Why? Because "language shapes attitudes".

Self-confidence is an attitude or state of mind. Although clients typically believe that self-confidence is acquired through accomplishments or achievements, we encourage them to look at self-confidence as a belief in one's self "knowing" that you can handle situations with assuredness and in a capable manner. Unfortunately, too many people do not believe in themselves and choose words that convey their ambivalence.

Does your communication convey confidence? Do you find yourself using words like "I think," "kind of," "maybe," "probably," or "just"? These words minimize the impact of your statements. This discredits your point of view; hence, people don't take you seriously. And you don't take you seriously!

Do you speak with assurance, or do your statements trail off into questions? This negates the definitive nature in the statement. It is important to make declarative statements. Keep your statements clear, concise, and to the point. There is no need to say it in a way that requires someone else's validation.

As you examine your linguistics, notice how many times you use words that denote indecision or ambivalence. Women frequently use words such as "try" or "think." The word try infers that you will make an attempt. Again, this type of speaking sets you up for failure. It sabotages your motivation because it intimates that you may not be successful. As Yoda in Star Wars said, "Do or do not. There is no *try*."

Consider the following statements:

- "I **will** try to diet."

- "I **will** try to pick it up after work."

- "I **will** try to get more sleep."

Now, take the "try" out of it.

- "I **will** diet."

- "I **will** pick it up after work."

- "I **will** get more sleep."

This sends the other person a clear-cut message. It also makes a statement that you believe in yourself and your ability to get these things done.

> *It creates confidence, which will make you more successful.*

The word "think" has the same connotation: "I think it would be a good idea if..." "I think this project needs..." "I think I will administer..." Omit the word "think" and listen to the difference in inflection.

If you lack self-confidence or if you find that these statements apply to you, we encourage you to practice the following:

Ask another person to "time you out" when they hear words like "just," "probably," "maybe," or "guess" or when they hear the words "think" or "try." We frequently use this in our group exercises and find that, on average, people will use these words sixteen times over a five-minute period! This exercise helps to increase awareness and change old patterns. Obviously, once you recognize that you use these words, it is important to repeat the sentence without the qualifier and with more confidence.

Your ability to speak confidently and assertively affects how others view you. It is imperative that you speak with authority. If words shape attitudes, then choose to use words that empower your belief in yourself and increase your confidence. You'll discover amazing results!

Using Your Head, Heart, and Gut

THREE OPERATING SYSTEMS TO BOLSTER YOUR DECISION MAKING

Once again, you already have everything you need to make the right decision.

 Women frequently report that they are unsure how to handle certain situations if they feel they have no control. For example, a woman might explain that her husband is not communicating with her and she doesn't know how to activate his communication skills. Another woman might complain about her boyfriend because he does nothing to advance the relationship. Sometimes it is a mother who doesn't know what to do to get her child to be more respectful, to stop using drugs, or to stop sneaking out of the house.

We believe that every woman possesses the ability to tap into her energy and know exactly what to do; however, they may feel powerless which interferes with their knowing. The problem is that she doesn't believe she knows what to do and, therefore, she lacks the confidence to make better decisions. She doesn't know that all the answers lie inside of her.

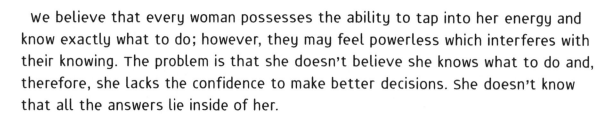

"LET NOTHING DISTURB THE HARMONY OF YOUR THOUGHTS" – LYDIA JUERGENSEN (CAROL'S GRANDMOTHER)

The formula for making healthy decisions is simple and guaranteed to be effective. It is a surefire method to access that "knowing." Every woman is incredibly astute in assessing situations. Perhaps it is her genetics from when the earth's earliest women were in charge of everyone's safety while the men were away hunting for food. She had to know how to manage the home, predict the children's next moves, watch for incoming blizzards, and fend off wild animals that could threaten the family's safety. She learned all these skills, but as usual, they felt so natural that she did not give herself credit for knowing them!

Fast forward thousands of years. The present-day woman has three operating mechanisms tucked inside of her that she can access at any time to get the answers. Once she learns the formula, she stops repeating destructive behaviors and starts navigating through life with more confidence.

The formula is actually quite simple, and you probably use one of the components when assessing what to do in a situation. The problem is that you likely are not using the entire process to make the best decision. we would ask you the following question to ascertain what comes most naturally to you: As you think of your own life, would you say you operate from your head (intellectually), from your heart (emotionally), or from your gut (intuitively)?

People who make the best decisions typically operate from all three. Your mind, emotions, and intuition should all be working together to formulate a reality-based plan that is user-friendly.

> ## *"NO ONE CAN MAKE YOU FEEL INFERIOR WITHOUT YOUR CONSENT"*
> ## *– ELEANOR ROOSEVELT*

PREDOMINANTLY USING YOUR HEAD

Perhaps you are the type of woman who operates from the head and relates to others in an intellectual way. Intellects know who they are. And, intellectually, they can reason what is happening to them, but they are disconnected from the negative outcomes that are emotionally occurring. They are completely disconnected from their intuition and consequently they are missing some important elements that help them to complete the puzzle to insure a
perfect fit. It affects their ability to commit because they haven't developed a comfortable relationship with their emotions. It's like the old saying, "You can't give what you don't have." Meaning, if you aren't comfortable with your emotions, you can't share them with someone else.

women who are predominantly "intellectualizers" primarily use thinking in their decision-making choices that are devoid of emotions or their intuition. As you might imagine, their relationships lack passion or emotion because these women "overthink" things. In addition, they are smart enough to know that something is missing in their lives but they just can't seem to identify what that is.

OPERATING PRIMARILY FROM YOUR HEART

Are you someone who chronically gets involved with the wrong person over and over again, never getting your needs met because you operate from your emotional part of yourself (heart) and you don't pay attention to what your intellect or your intuition is telling you about the situation? Do you recognize early on in the relationship that this person is not giving back to you the time, attention, or money that you are giving to him or her? And yet you continue to ignore the signs (intellect) in the hope that there will be a payback someday?

Women who operate solely from their emotions will continue to let their feelings direct the course. When it comes to healthy relationships, you must pay attention to how you are treated and how you respect each other. In healthy love, you have mutually developed goals and you have shared values that contribute to the relationship. If you allow your emotions to rule your course, you will most likely end up fully loving the other person but not really loving yourself. Women who solely operate from their hearts have difficulty finding the right person in their life. They possess "good gut," but they don't listen to that nagging feeling they get about a person. Their intellect may also be developed, but they quickly dismiss it and let their heart do the directing.

NOT PAYING ATTENTION TO YOUR GUT

Every woman has been given the gift of intuition, but she may not have been trained to pay attention to what her gut is telling her. Intuition is that inner "feeling or knowing" about someone or something. It's when you sense something subconsciously or unconsciously. It's an internal sense or awareness that "The phone is about to ring" or "That person is going to hurt you" or "That business deal is not the right one." Historically, we believe that mothers have an innately well-developed sense of intuition—critical for the survival of their young.

Some of you may say that you don't have that skill. Most likely you do have it, but you haven't yet recognized it inside of you. Intuition is a wonderful tool to operate from; however, most people have not been encouraged to listen to it or develop it. Intuition is really the ability to assess a situation and "know what to do about it." When women make decisions about their relationships by accessing their intuition, they are more inclined to make healthier choices.

This skill can be enhanced by paying special attention to signs that are intuitive. Some women say they know when they feel a feeling, or when something tugs at them, or when the answer just comes to them that they are using their intuition. Others say that once they quiet their environment and their thoughts and focus, they hear the answer or the guidance they need. The key to developing your intuition is to get quiet and wait for the response. It is a type of meditative process in which you become connected to the knowing inside of you. Many describe it as a spiritual process finding that deep connection within.

There are many books on the intuitive process that recommend ways to access this gift more readily. It is also important to learn about it so you are more equipped to pass it on to your daughters (and sons). Think about it: How often do you ask your daughter to search inside of herself to find the answer?

There are some women who have trained themselves to use all three of these powerful internal tools; however, many women gravitate to only using one. If you want to make smarter decisions, have healthier relationships, and deal more positively with the world, work to develop each one of these assets. As you begin, know that it will take some practice to be cognizant and to use all three of your tools.

Take some time right now and contemplate which skill you use the most. Are your decisions intellectually based or heart-driven, or do you operate from a gut feeling? Now, decide which skill you use least. Are you afraid to trust your emotions? Do you ignore your gut feelings, or do you reject your own thoughts and reasoning abilities? Needless to say, the skill that you use the least is the one that will require the most development.

USING THE HEAD, HEART, AND GUT FORMULA

write out a situation or problem that has consistently occurred in your life.

_____

_____

_____

_____

_____

BREAK THE PROBLEM DOWN AND ASK YOURSELF THE FOLLOWING:

what do I think about this problem and what do I need to do about it as I reason it out?

_____

_____

_____

_____

_____

How do I feel about this situation and what do my emotions drive me to do?

_____

_____

_____

_____

_____

_____

After getting quiet and thinking about the situation, what does my gut tell me to do?

_____

_____

_____

_____

_____

_____

After you have written about the situation and you have written your responses, you will notice that two of the gifts support each other. whenever there is agreement from two of the tools, it is an automatic direction for how you need to handle the situation.

Let's look at a common problem that a woman was facing and watch how she applied the "Head, Heart, and Gut" formula to get more clarity in her life.

Jamie was a thirty-nine-year-old, attractive, bright female who had never been married and had a history of unsuccessful relationships with men. She was a very compassionate woman who appeared to have everything going for her. She had a good job making six figures. She had her master's degree in business. She owned her own home. She loved to cook and take care of others. She seemingly had everything going for her, except that she desperately wanted a relationship and had difficulty finding anyone who would date her longer than three months.

As she searched for patterns in her interaction with men, it became apparent that as soon as she started dating a man, she would inundate him with expectations. As soon as the end of the first week and sometimes even the first date, she would start assessing whether he was marriage material. She would begin to expect daily phone calls and frequent dates. She would have sex with him within the first two dates and then assume that she had the commitment she so desperately needed. She would quickly tell him that she expected to hear from him by wednesday if they were to go out by Friday, and then she would act disgruntled if he did not meet her deadlines. Her over-dependence ended up pushing each man away. Because he had not really established a solid connection with her, he would typically try to fade out of the picture, which would then result in a rant about the double messages he had sent to her.

Since she was able to cite at least twelve relationships that had ended up disappointing her, she was willing to assess things using the Head, Heart, and Gut formula.

Here was the work that she did:

- Intellectual Aptitude—What does she think when she uses her head?

  "When I think through things intellectually, I realize that I am moving faster in the relationship than the men I date. I don't give them enough time to plan the dates or call me. I know that men need to feel like they are in control, and I know that I tend to want to teach them how to date."

- Emotionally—How did she feel when she used her heart?

  "I am tired of being alone and I want someone to love me. When I get into relationships, I want to be pursued and so I shower them with affection hoping to get that in return. What I want most in my life is to be loved and cared for."

- Intuition—What does her intuition and gut tell her?

  "My gut tells me to slow down and let the guy make the plans. Even before I start to text, I wonder if I should let them text me first, but I just can't stop myself, so I initiate contact. All my friends tell me to stop fantasizing about what could be and to stay in the moment, but I am afraid that if I don't stay on top of things, I will be ignored or forgotten, so I move it along a bit. My gut tells me to have faith that I will find the right guy or that God will take care of this, but I would rather do it myself."

In Jamie's scenario her head is telling her to slow down, her heart is telling her to find someone who will love her, and her gut is telling her to have faith that things will turn out if she stops working at it so hard.

You can clearly see that in this scenario, Jamie's need to be loved was sabotaging the very thing that she wanted. Her emotions were clearly driving her actions and getting in the way of her desired outcome. When she could see with clarity what was happening, she was able to understand that her work would entail using more of her head and her gut energy while she practiced dating.

This would invariably get her the outcome she wanted. She needed to start practicing using her intellect and her intuition to create the life she deserved.

It took fourteen months, but once Jamie learned to use her head and her gut in combination with her heart, she was able to meet a man who loved her unconditionally and one she could depend on with certainty.

This simple formula is another tool that you can add to your tool belt, because when things aren't working, it makes sense to try something that does. And what better tools to use but the special gifts we have been given—like your head, our heart, and our gut!

10. You Have Changed!

"EVERYONE HAS INSIDE OF HER A PIECE OF GOOD NEWS. THE GOOD NEWS IS THAT YOU DON'T KNOW HOW GREAT YOU CAN BE, HOW MUCH YOU CAN LOVE, WHAT YOU CAN ACCOMPLISH, AND WHAT YOUR POTENTIAL IS. – ANNE FRANK

Sometimes fear will keep you from doing the things you need to do to sustain real change. This workbook was designed to help you create the life you deserve! So often, women are so busy that they ignore that "knowing inside" that they have a passion or purpose to do something extraordinary in their life. Now that you are a healthier woman, think about whether something has been tugging at your heartstrings to accomplish but you didn't have the ability to proceed with confidence.

WE WANT TO INVITE YOU TO DEEPLY CONSIDER . . .

when things get quiet and the distractions are few, is there a nagging feeling that continues to haunt you, reminding you that there is a calling you are choosing to ignore?

well you only live once, so it is absolutely your responsibility to make the most of your life. This life is not a dress rehearsal. This statement implies that you need to "go for the gusto" and move beyond the fears that may keep you a bystander in your own life.

This requires that you make a concerted effort to "stretch" or "move out of your comfort zone." Inevitably, when you choose to stretch, you are making a choice to do something different. This will give you a taste of something new and lead you through a growth experience. It adds to your repertoire of life experiences and it increases your life skills. we tell women they don't need to be successful. Their success comes not from the outcome but from moving from one comfort zone to the next level, which usually involves taking risks, practicing different skills and stretching out of your comfort zone. In other words, it's not the outcome; it's the effort a person makes to do something different that creates sustained change.

Having said that, we also believe it's imperative that you have a game plan to get you where you are going. If you consistently feel that little gnawing reminder that you need to be doing something new, you must plan for that.

Is there something in your life that you would love to pursue, but you either don't know how to make it happen or your fear keeps you from doing it? On the next page, we invite you to deeply consider...

WHAT HAS BEEN TUGGING AT YOUR HEARTSTRINGS?

We have worked with thousands of women who, in the course of their treatment or coaching, have identified things they have always wanted to do. Unfortunately, there are limiting beliefs that interrupt pursuit of these dreams. This workbook is an opportunity to listen to your intuition and follow through with your dreams. And again, as Marianne Williamson says, "Your playing small does not serve the world."

And the Journey Continues...

"FOR ME, BECOMING ISN'T ABOUT ARRIVING SOMEWHERE OR ACHIEVING A CERTAIN AIM. I SEE IT INSTEAD AS FORWARD MOTION, A MEANS OF EVOLVING, A WAY TO REACH CONTINUOUSLY TOWARD A BETTER SELF. THE JOURNEY DOESN'T END." — MICHELLE OBAMA

Now that you have completed this workbook, you are able to see your progress and acknowledge it. we believe that you are a much different woman now than when you first started.

we applaud the time you have spent improving your skills and know that you will be much more likely to get your needs met because of all your hard work. Our mission is to improve the lives of women by raising awareness and teaching the skills necessary to change lives.

we are tremendously grateful to the countless women who have imprinted our lives so deeply, especially the thousands of women clients who we have had the honor to accompany along their personal journeys throughout the decades.

May your journey be richly blessed as you also improve the lives of the people you impact...especially your daughters, mothers, and girlfriends!

- Carol & Christine

Carol and Christine are available to conduct trainings on self-esteem, women's issues, and anxiety/emotion regulation as well as many other topics.

"I CHOOSE TO MAKE THE REST OF MY LIFE THE BEST OF MY LIFE."
— LOUISE HAY

BIBLIOGRAPHY

Beattie, Melody. *Codependent No More: How to Stop Controlling Others and Start Caring for Yourself.* Center City, MN: Hazelden Foundation, 1986.

Canfield, Jack. *The Success Principles: How to Get from Where You Are to Where You Want to Be.* New York, NY: Harper Collins Publishers, 2004.

Dyer, Wayne. *The Power of Intention: Learning to Co-create Your World Your Way.* Carlsbad, CA: Hay House Inc., 2005.

Hanson, Rick. *Just One Thing: Developing a Buddha Brain One Simple Practice at a Time.* Oakland, CA: New Harbinger Publications, Inc., 2011.

Lerner, Harriet. *The Dance of Anger: A Woman's Guide to Changing the Patterns of Intimate Relationships.* New York, NY: Harper & Row Publishers Inc., 1985.

Richardson, Cheryl. *The Art of Extreme Self-Care: 12 Practical and Inspiring Ways to Love Yourself More.* Carlsbad, CA: Hay House Inc., 2019.

---. *Stand Up for Your Life: A Practical Step-by-Step Plan to Build Inner Confidence and Personal Power.* New York, NY: Free Press, 2002.

Van der Kolk, Bessel. *The Body Keeps the Score: Brain, Mind, and Body in the Healing of Trauma.* London, UK: Penguin Books, 2014.

About Carol

Carol Juergensen Sheets, ACSW, LCSW, CSAT, CCPS-C, PCC is a highly regarded social worker, personal life coach and a renowned self-help author who brings a variety of experiences to her clients and readers including having worked in schools, hospitals and in mental health for over 40 years. She has worked for 4 decades facilitating thousands of groups for women and teens. Additionally, Carol has devoted the last 2 decades to helping men and women manage their sex addiction and helping betrayed partners work through the trauma of sexual and relational betrayal. She is a well respected sex and relationship therapist to individuals and couples across the country and beyond.

Carol completed her master's degree at the honorable institution, Indiana University School of Social Work. She is currently facilitating popular workshops on relationships both statewide and nationally. Carol does annual workshops for the International Institute for Trauma and Addiction Professionals. She is also a revered trainer for the Association of Partners of Sex Addicts Trauma Specialists and is a consultant for clinicians and coaches for APSATS.

Carol very much enjoys facilitating group and couples work and has facilitated thousands of groups in the last 3 decades. She has been a highly sought-after executive and life coach for over 15 years and loves motivating her clients to reach their greatest potential.

Carol's breakout book *Help. Her. Heal.* has been sold in countries around the world including Canada, Denmark, Japan, England, France and Australia. Primarily written for male partners of wives, fiancées and girlfriends (yet also extremely helpful for females and couples), *Help. Her. Heal.* deals with assisting men with problematic sexual behavior to develop their relational skills to help their partners heal through the powerful use of empathy.

Help. Her. Heal. explores the necessity for the sex addict to work on both his individual recovery needs and his relational skills. So that addicts will be able to navigate through the devastation caused by sexual addiction, Carol teaches her all-important signature formula AVR, which is Acknowledging the issue, Validating the primary feeling, and then Reassuring the betrayed partner of the changes that are being made.

The book beautifully addresses how men can access and develop empathy for their female partners, particularly checking in with their partner's fears and needs and practicing healthy behaviors and practices. The book aids men in how to deal with conflict after betrayal, as well as techniques to stay strong while they help their partners heal. Finally, *Help. Her. Heal.* deftly addresses the complex rituals of connection, trust and restoration that can heal a broken relationship.

Carol believes in teaching people how to live their best lives in romance and in life in general. She has hosted radio shows and podcasts over her entire professional career. Also known as "Carol the Coach", Carol hosts www.blogtalkradio.com/sexhelpwithcarolthecoach to help her listeners understand the complexities of sexual addiction and partner betrayal. She also hosts a podcast specifically for partners to navigate through the trauma of sexual betrayal called, www.blogtalkradio.com/betrayalrecoveryradio for APSATS.org.

Carol also hosts highly productive teleseminars that feature goal setting, relationship building and shortcuts to positive self-esteem.

Carol has written columns in newspapers and magazines to help people grow emotionally and enhance their well-being. You can read over 500 articles on her website www.carolthecoach.com or go to her sex addiction website for sex addicts or partners at: www.sexhelpwithcarolthecoach.com

When asked about her profession, Carol says: "I have been blessed to help people all over the world! My work has been a platform for psychotherapy, speaking engagements, radio and television, newspaper and magazine articles and now the books that are helping men and women heal. Early on in my life I learned that my passion was to help people navigate through the trauma of their childhood and adult life and to move them into post-traumatic growth where they would develop resiliency and actualize their potential."

Carol Juergensen Sheets is a best-selling author for the esteemed publishing company Sano Press.

Carol Juergensen Sheets ACSW, LCSW, CSAT, CCPS-C, PCC
EMDR Certified Therapist
Strategic Coaching and Therapies
3815 River Crossing Pkwy, Suite 100 Indianapolis, IN 46240
(317) 847-2244 | carol@carolthecoach.com

About Christine

Christine Turo-Shields, ACSW, LCSW, LCAC brings hope and humor, energy and enthusiasm to her work with children, families and adults. For over 30 years, she has provided therapy in a variety of settings, including individual, marital, family and group counseling. Her expertise is rich with various clinical passion areas, including women's empowerment, anxiety/panic disorders, depression, abuse/trauma/PTSD, addictions as well as with those who are gifted/profoundly gifted. Blending CBT with mindfulness and hope for the future, Christine brings people to a place of recovery and restoration, whatever their struggle may be, including an exploration of aspects of faith and spirituality amidst their journey of life.

Christine completed her master's degree at Indiana University School of Social Work where the values of empowerment and self-care were deeply imprinted upon her. She is statewide and national workshop presenter on a variety of clinical topics including women's issues, post-traumatic growth, trauma and survivor loss recovery, faith and spirituality, anxiety management as well as the blessings and burdens of the gifted and their families.

She is an avid believer in the power of healing through groups and has facilitated thousands of women's and teen groups with Carol Juergensen Sheets over the last 3 decades. She currently facilitates a group for gifted women who struggle with anxiety and depression as well as an emotion regulation/anxiety management group. She was extremely blessed and honored to facilitate a post-traumatic growth group for those who had experienced the loss of a loved one from a traumatic death—it was one of the most profound and humbling experiences of her professional career.

Christine is certified in EMDR Therapy (Eye Movement Desensitization and Reprocessing), which is a highly effective treatment for trauma. As an Indiana State Board Member of the American Foundation for Suicide Prevention (AFSP), she works extensively with survivors of suicide loss, including providing suicide prevention trainings at local churches, schools and interested organizations. She also has clinical specialty with women suffer with perinatal mood disorders, and she has been a guest presenter for Postpartum Support International (PSI) Indianapolis training regarding the effectiveness of EMDR for those who have experienced birth trauma or have had a history of sexual abuse.

Additionally, she is a nationally trained provider for the National Center for Missing & Exploited Children and is a member of NCMEC's Family Advocacy Outreach Network, providing therapeutic services and support to local families with missing and exploited children to address family trauma, reunification and adjustment.

As a co-owner of Kenosis Counseling Center, Inc., a community-based private practice, she provides clinical supervision to graduate interns as well as professionals who are working towards licensure. Guiding them as they develop clinical skills, she encourages professional caregivers to also make self-care a priority, become more mindful, and practice balance in order that they thrive rather than exist. She has received training through Vanderbilt's Distressed Physicians Program and has worked to support physicians as they navigate professional pressures. Christine believes that daily investment in self enhances a one's ability to tend to others' needs both personally and professionally over the long-term.

Transformations is her inaugural book. She is excited to launch her second co-authored book, *Unleashing Your Power: Moving Through the Trauma of Partner Betrayal.* She is also currently in creation of future books, *Calming the Calamities* as well as *A Soul's Search for Meaning.*

As a consummate extrovert, Christine is always open to providing trainings...to inquire, you can email her at christine@kenosiscenter.com or visit the website www.kenosiscenter.com

Christine Tyro-Shields ACSW, LCSW, LCAC

EMDR Certified Therapist
Kenosis Counseling Center, Inc.
1678 Fry Road, Suite D. Greenwood, IN 46142
(317) 865-1674 | christine@kenosiscenter.com

Made in the USA
Las Vegas, NV
16 August 2021